Questions & A

O LEVEL CHEMISTRY

J. Sheen
B.A., Grad. I.E.R.E.

Checkmate/Arnold

First published in Great Britain 1984 by
Checkmate Publications,
4 Ainsdale Close, Bromborough, Wirral L63 0EU.

This edition published in association with
Edward Arnold (Publishers) Ltd.,
41 Bedford Square, London WC1B 3DQ

Edward Arnold (Australia) Pty Ltd.,
80 Waverley Road, Caulfield East,
Victoria 3145, Australia

Edward Arnold, 3 East Read Street,
Baltimore, Maryland 21202, USA.

ISBN 0 946973 27 X

Printed and bound by Richard Clay (The Chaucer Press),
Bungay, Suffolk

INTRODUCTION

This book is designed for students who are preparing themselves for the GCE/CSE 'O' Level examination in Chemistry. It comprises typical extended answer examination questions based on current examination board papers.

The examination questions are designed to give candidates the opportunity of demonstrating depth of understanding of the chemical materials. Candidates are also expected to be able to organise and present ideas in a clear and logical form. Communication of ideas and understanding play a great part in the achievement of good examination results.

This book, when used in conjunction with the appropriate text book and study notes, acts as a guide in tackling examination questions and forms a good basis for revision.

John Sheen

DATA FOR CHEMISTRY PAPERS

Element	Atomic number	Symbol	Relative atomic mass	Element	Atomic number	Symbol	Relative atomic mass
Aluminium	13	Al	27	Lead	82	Pb	207
Antimony	51	Sb	122	Lithium	3	Li	7
Argon	18	Ar	40	Magnesium	12	Mg	24
Arsenic	33	As	75	Manganese	25	Mn	55
Barium	56	Ba	137	Mercury	80	Hg	200
Beryllium	4	Be	9	Neon	10	Ne	20
Bismuth	83	Bi	209	Nickel	28	Ni	59
Boron	5	B	11	Nitrogen	7	N	14
Bromine	35	Br	80	Oxygen	8	O	16
Cadmium	48	Cd	112.5	Phosphorus	15	P	31
Calcium	20	Ca	40	Platinum	78	Pt	195
Carbon	6	C	12	Potassium	19	K	39
Chlorine	17	Cl	35.5	Selenium	34	Se	79
Chromium	24	Cr	52	Silicon	14	Si	28
Cobalt	27	Co	59	Silver	47	Ag	108
Copper	29	Cu	63.5	Sodium	11	Na	23
Fluorine	9	F	19	Strontium	38	Sr	88
Germanium	32	Ge	72.5	Sulphur	16	S	32
Gold	79	Au	197	Tin	50	Sn	119
Helium	2	He	4	Titanium	22	Ti	48
Hydrogen	1	H	1	Vanadium	23	V	51
Iodine	53	I	127	Xenon	54	Xe	131
Iron	26	Fe	56	Zinc	30	Zn	65
Krypton	36	Kr	84				

TABLE OF CONTENTS

Question 1   (20 marks)   (Answer page 16)

Name each of the possible substances indicated by the letters and give equations for each of the reactions given below:

(a)   When a colourless gas **A** was burned in air, two gaseous products were formed. When cooled one of these gaseous products gave a colourless liquid **B**. The colourless gas **A**, when passed through liquid bromine, formed a colourless compound **C**.

(b)   Sodium hydroxide solution when warmed with a white solid **D** gave off a gas **E** which caused damp red litmus paper to turn blue. A white precipitate **F** was formed when silver nitrate solution was added to a solution of **D**.

(c)   When a solution **G** had sodium carbonate added to it a colourless gas **G** was given off which formed a white precipitate when passed through limewater. When solution **G** had barium chloride solution added to it a white precipitate **J** was formed.

Question 2   (20 marks)   (Answer page 18)

(a)   (i)   Explain why one acid may be 'weaker' or 'stronger' than another. Name an example of each type.

      (ii)   Hydrochloric acid is said to be a monoprotic acid; what is meant by this?

(b)   (i)   Describe what happens when zinc reacts with a strong acid giving an ionic equation for the reaction.

      (ii)   State any differences in your observations if a weak acid were used instead of a strong acid in the above reaction.

(c)   State two properties of an acid, giving an equation for each example.

Question 3   **(25 marks)**   (Answer page 19)

(a)   Describe in detail what you would observe when malachite (green copper compound $CuCO_3 . Cu(OH)_2$) is heated strongly in a test tube. Explain how you would identify any gases formed in the reaction.

(b)   What method would you employ to show that copper is contained in the malachite?

(c)   Describe carefully an experiment to show how you would determine the formula of the residue of the malachite after it was strongly heated. Explain how the results of your experiment would be used to calculate the formula of the residue.

Question 4   **(25 marks)**   (Answer page 22)

(a)   Describe fully how you would prepare some crystals of copper (II) sulphate, $CuSO_4 . 5H_2O$, starting from copper (II) oxide.

(b)   Describe and explain what happens when these crystals are heated.

(c)   Choosing either copper (II) sulphate or copper (II) chloride describe what can be seen when a solution of the copper salt is electrolysed, using carbon electrodes. Give equations to represent the electrode reactions that take place.

Question 5   **(25 marks)**   (Answer page 24)

(a)   An oxide of lead was found to contain 90.8% of lead by mass. Calculate the formula of this oxide.

(b)   What gas might be used in the process of reducing a sample of lead oxide to lead?

Describe carefully an experiment to show how you would determine the formula of a given sample of an oxide of lead. Include in your explanation a labelled diagram of the apparatus and explain how the results of your experiment would be used to calculate the formula of the oxide.

Question 6 [20 marks] (Answer page 26)

(a) Describe with the aid of a labelled diagram one method of preparing hydrogen in the laboratory.

(b) Calculate the volume of hydrogen at room temperature and pressure which would be needed to reduce 5g of copper (II) oxide to copper (relative atomic masses: $O = 16$, $Cu = 64$; one mole of any gas at room temperature and pressure occupies 24000 cm^3).

(c) When hydrogen is burned in air water is produced. Describe with the aid of a diagram how this water is collected and also give an account of a test to show that the liquid obtained is pure water.

(d) Hydrogen is less dense than air. When a gas jar of hydrogen is inverted over a gas jar of air, after a period of time the composition of the mixture of gases in each gas jar becomes the same and then remains constant. Explain why this is so.

Question 7 [25 marks] (Answer page 28)

(a) Give one equation in each case for sulphuric acid acting as (i) an acid, (ii) a dehydrating agent, (iii) an oxidising agent.

(b) By evaporating the solution obtained on neutralising sodium hydroxide solution with dilute sulphuric acid, it is possible to isolate a crystalline solid. By changing the relative volumes of the two reagents a different solid product can be obtained. Explain how this occurs giving equations for the reactions involved.

(c) Zinc (symbol Zn) reacts with sulphuric acid releasing hydrogen sulphide:

$$4\ Zn + 5\ H_2SO_4 \rightarrow 4\ ZnSO_4 + 4\ H_2O + H_2S$$

It was found that 13g of zinc reacted exactly with

25 cm³ of 10 M sulphuric acid. Calculate the mass of zinc which reacts with 5 moles of sulphuric acid. Then use the equation to deduce the relative atomic mass of zinc.

Question 8 [25 marks]   (Answer page 30)

Some reactions of nitric acid are shown in outline below:

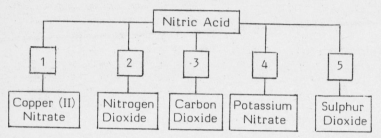

Explain how the reactions 1, 2, 3, 4 and 5 may occur in order that samples of each product may be obtained. Include for each reaction, the names of the substances used, reaction conditions and concentration of the nitric acid.

Question 9 [20 marks]   (Answer page 31)

(a) (i)   Describe how ethene is obtained from crude oil.

     (ii) Describe a polymer which can be made from ethene molecules. Give diagrams of the monomer and polymer.

(b) Name the product, giving its structural formula, when ethene is passed into bromine water. What would be observed in this reaction?

(c) Draw diagrams of the three isomers of the alkane having the molecular formula C_5H_{12}.

(d) The heat evolved when one mole of ethanol is completely burned is 1370 kJ. What is the minimum mass of ethanol which must be burned to heat 1 kg of water from 25°C to 95°C? (Relative atomic masses: H = 1, C = 12, O = 16. 4.18 kJ will heat 1 kg of water through 1°C)

Question 10 [20 marks]   (Answer page 34)

For each of the following, write equations for the chemical reactions taking place and explain any differences in the reactions:

(a) When dilute sulphuric acid is added to sodium carbonate crystals the reaction is vigorous, effervescence occurs and a colourless solution is formed. When the same dilute sulphuric acid is added to pieces of calcium carbonate the reaction is less vigorous with little effervescence and the reaction stops quickly leaving a white solid.

(b) Iron reacts with copper (II) sulphate solution but not with magnesium sulphate solution.

(c) Using the same apparatus and applying the same voltage, a larger current flows through a M solution of hydrochloric acid than through a M solution of ethanoic acid.

(d) When sodium hydroxide solution is added to separate solutions of zinc chloride and iron (III) chloride, both form a precipitate at first. When an excess of the alkali is added to the separate solutions, the precipitate from the iron (III) chloride does not dissolve but that from the zinc chloride does dissolve.

Question 11 [20 marks]   (Answer page 37)

(a) **(i)** Name a solid which will catalyse the decomposition of hydrogen peroxide and give a definition of a catalyst.

     (ii) Write an equation for the decomposition of hydrogen peroxide.

    (iii) What experiments would you carry out to investigate the effect of the solid catalyst on hydrogen peroxide? State the observations made and give the results of the experiments which confirm that the solid was acting as a catalyst.

(b) State two reactions which are affected by exposure to light.

(c) Changing the pressure of reacting gases affects their rates of reaction. Explain why this is so.

Question 12 **[20 marks]**   (Answer page 39)

For each substance listed below:

(a) Name one substance which exhibits the properties given.

(b) State the structure of the substance, i.e. whether metallic, ionic, molecular, macromolecular.

(c) State a reason for choosing the structure.

(1) Substance J - Crystalline solid which on heating forms a purple vapour. Some of this forms crystals on the cooler parts of the tube and the rest condenses lower down the tube.

(2) Substance K - Solid, non-conductor of electricity, dissolves in water to give a solution which conducts electricity well.

(3) Substance L - Solid, good conductor of electricity, displaces hydrogen rapidly from cold dilute acids but very slowly from cold water.

(4) Substance M - Solid, good conductor of electricity, when heated burns while in the solid state forming a product which is gaseous at room temperature.

(5) Substance N - A gas - very soluble in water, good conductor of electricity when in solution, turns litmus paper red.

Question 13 **[25 marks]**   (Answer page 40)

(a) Describe the industrial electrolysis of brine. Include in your answer a labelled diagram and equations for the reactions taking place at each electrode.

(b) Name all the products of this electrolytic process and state two important uses for each of them.

Question 14 **[20 marks]**   (Answer page 43)

(a) Draw diagrams showing the bonding in molecules of the following substances:

(1) Ethene   (2) Carbon Dioxide
(3) Ammonia   (4) Water

A single covalent bond should be represented by a single line between two atoms and a double bond by two lines between atoms. State also whether each compound exists as a solid, liquid or gas at room temperature and pressure.

(b) State four different ways in which simple covalent and ionic compounds differ.

(c) Sodium chloride is an ionic crystal; explain how the sodium and chlorine are bonded to form the crystalline structure at room temperature and pressure.

(d) Sodium chloride and magnesium oxide are ionic compounds. Give reasons why sodium chloride has a much lower melting point than magnesium oxide.

(e) Carbon is polymorphic. Explain why, in its crystalline form of diamond, its melting point is higher than 3000°C.

Question 15 **[20 marks]**   (Answer page 46)

Explain the meaning and effect on the environment of each of the following:

(a) The "Greenhouse Effect".

(b) Lead pollution.
(c) Acid rain.
(d) Fertiliser pollution.

Question 16 [20 marks]   (Answer page 48)

(a) Ethanol for use in alcoholic drinks is made by the fermentation process. Outline this process and give equations for the reactions occurring.

(b) Ethanol for industrial use is manufactured from crude oil. Outline each stage of the process naming the reagents and necessary conditions.

(c) An organic compound comprising 50.0% oxygen, 12.5% hydrogen and 37.5% carbon has a relative molecular mass of 32. Calculate the molecular formula of the compound and work out its structural formula.

(Relative atomic masses: O = 16, H = 1, C = 12)

Question 17 [20 marks]   (Answer page 50)

(a) There are several ways of preparing soluble salts; state three methods of preparation giving the products of each reaction.

(b) **(i)** Describe the preparation of crystals of magnesium sulphate (soluble salt) from magnesium oxide. Give an equation for the reaction.

(ii) Describe the preparation of magnesium carbonate (insoluble salt) from magnesium sulphate. Give an equation for the reaction.

(c) Describe tests that could be carried out on the above preparations to indicate:

(i)   a sulphate
(ii)   a carbonate

had been obtained.

Question 18 [25 marks]   (Answer page 52)

Air comprises the following gases: oxygen, nitrogen, carbon dioxide, water vapour, argon and neon which are useful raw materials.

(a) For any three of these gases, describe simple experiments that could be carried out to demonstrate their presence in the air.

(b) Give an outline of two industrial processes which use air as a raw material but make use of a different gas from the air. Explain the chemical principles involved in each process and clearly indicate which gas from the air is used.

Question 19 [25 marks]   (Answer page 55)

Three organic compounds F, G and K are described below. Each compound has two carbon atoms in its molecule.

(i) F is a colourless gas which burns with a luminous flame. It also decolourises bromine water.

(ii) G is a colourless liquid which reacts with sodium hydrogencarbonate to give a colourless gas J which turns lime water milky. It also reacts with magnesium to give the flammable gas H.

(iii) K is a colourless liquid which burns readily in air. It reacts with sodium to produce a flammable gas H but it has no action on litmus paper.

Identify substances F, G, H, J, K and give equations for all the reactions described.

Describe how K could be converted into <u>either</u> F <u>or</u> G.

Question 20 [20 marks]   (Answer page 57)

(a) Explain how iron is manufactured by reducing iron ore in a blast furnace. Include in your explanation, giving equations, how **(i)** the ore is reduced; **(ii)** a slag is formed and removed; **(iii)** the energy for this process is produced.

(b) State two differences in composition between pig iron and steel.

(c) Blocks of magnesium are fitted to underground steel pipes. Explain how this helps to prevent corrosion of the pipes.

(d) Explain how a metal, used in a different way to magnesium in the prevention of rusting, works on an article of your choice.

Question 21 [25 marks] (Answer page 60)

The following changes may be brought about by performing simple experiments. Describe experiments to show that:

(a) Sulphite ions are changed to sulphur dioxide molecules.

(b) Ammonium ions are changed to ammonia molecules.

(c) Hydrogen ions are changed to hydrogen molecules.

(d) Chlorine molecules are changed to chloride ions.

Give the starting materials for each experiment and any equations for the reactions. Describe pertinent points in the reactions.

Question 22 [25 marks] (Answer page 62)

(a) Explain, with reference to a named example, what an ester is. Give the full structural formula of the ester and explain how it may be prepared in the laboratory.

(b) Describe how soap is manufactured from fats and how it is separated out.

(c) Describe and explain the advantages that modern detergents have over soaps.

Question 23 [25 marks]   (Answer page 65)

The behaviour of three substances, H, J and L are described below:

(a)   A white solid H gave a yellow flame test. When heated with excess dilute hydrochloric acid, sulphur dioxide was evolved and a colourless solution was left. When the colourless solution was evaporated to dryness a white solid I remained.

(b)   When a black powder J was dissolved in dilute nitric acid a blue solution K was formed and no gas was evolved. On heating the solution, water vapour was evolved and a blue solid remained. When the blue solid was heated strongly it changed into a black powder and a mixture of nitrogen dioxide and oxygen was evolved.

(c)   When metal L was heated in a stream of dry hydrogen chloride, hydrogen gas was evolved and a white solid M was left. When the same metal L was heated in dry chlorine, a dark red solid N was formed. M and N were dissolved separately in water and sodium hydroxide solution was added to solution M and also to solution N. Solution M gave a green precipitate and solution N gave a brown precipitate.

Identify the substances H, I, J, K, L, M and N giving equations for each reaction.

Describe tests you would use to identify the gases: sulphur dioxide, nitrogen dioxide and hydrogen.

Question 24 [25 marks]   (Answer page 67)

Atmospheric nitrogen is used in the preparation of large amounts of ammonia and nitric acid for use in the manufacture of nitrogenous fertilisers.

(a)   Describe the manufacture of ammonia and nitric acid.

(b)   Explain, with reference to the nitrogen cycle, why nitrogen compounds are added to cultivated land.

(c) In terms of nitrogen content show, by calculation, which is the better fertiliser, sodium nitrate or ammonium sulphate.

Question 25 [25 marks]　　　　　(Answer page 71)

Describe how you would separate the constituents of each of the following mixtures in order to obtain pure samples of each component.

(a) Copper (II) oxide and carbon.

(b) Ammonium chloride and sodium chloride.

(c) A blue dye from a mixture of other dyes which together form black ink.

(d) Carbon monoxide and carbon dioxide.

(e) Almost pure ethanol from a mixture with water.

Question 26 [20 marks]　　　　　(Answer page 75)

(a) What is meant by the following terms:

(i) electrolysis; (ii) electrolyte; (iii) non-electrolyte;

(iv) strong electrolyte; (v) weak electrolyte;

(vi) anion; (vii) cation.

(b) Describe how you would proceed to electrolyse a solution of copper (II) chloride.

Make a labelled diagram of the arrangement of apparatus you would use.

Describe what would be seen and give equations for any electrode reactions.

Question 27 [25 marks]　　　　　(Answer page 77)

(a) The heat of formation of water is -286 kJ mol^{-1}. Explain the meaning of this statement giving suitable equations and energy level diagrams.

/continued......

(b) When 4g of sodium hydroxide was dissolved in $100cm^3$ of distilled water in a heat insulating beaker the temperature fall was 10 K.

Show that the heat of solution of the hydroxide is -42.0 kJ mol^{-1}.

(The specific heat capacity of water = 4.2 J g^{-1} $°C^{-1}$.)

Question 28 [25 marks]   (Answer page 80)

(a) Describe fully the changes that take place when powdered sulphur is gradually heated to its melting point.

(b) Mention briefly the proof that rhombic and mono-clinic sulphur are allotropes.

(c) Calculate the mass of sulphur which, on complete combustion, would yield 7 dm^3 of sulphur dioxide measured at 182°C and 722 mm Hg pressure.

Question 29 [20 marks]   (Answer page 81)

(a) Describe what is meant by

(i)   a saturated solution
(ii) a supersaturated solution
(iii) solubility

(b) Use the solubility curves and table overleaf to answer the following:

(i)   A mixture of 135g of potassium nitrate and 32g of sodium chloride is dissolved in 100g of water at 70°C.

What amount of potassium nitrate separates out on cooling to 20°C?

What amount of sodium chloride separates out on cooling to 20°C?

(ii) A mixture of 95g of potassium nitrate and 95g of sodium chloride is dissolved in 100g of water at 70°C.

/continued......

What amount of potassium nitrate separates out on cooling to 20°C?

What amount of sodium chloride separates out on cooling to 20°C?

(iii) A mixture of 32g of potassium chlorate with 32g of potassium chloride is dissolved in 100g of water at 70°C.

What amount of potassium chlorate separates out on cooling to 20°C?

What amount of potassium chloride separates out on cooling to 20°C?

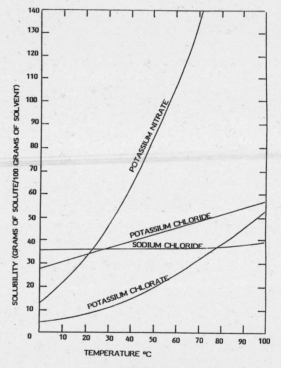

SOLUBILITY CURVES

	Potassium Nitrate/g	Sodium Chloride/g	Potassium Chlorate/g	Potassium Chloride/g
Solubility at 70°C	140	37	32	48
Solubility at 20°C	32	35	8	34

<u>Question 30</u> **[20 marks]**   (Answer page 82)

(a)   What is the difference between temporary and perm-
      anent hardness of water and what causes each kind
      of hardness?

(b)   Explain how both kinds of hardness can be removed
      from water.

(c)   Give two examples of the advantages and disadvantages
      of hard water.

Question 1

(a) Ethene is a member of the **homologous** series of hydrocarbons called alkenes. It is a colourless gas which burns in air giving water vapour and carbon dioxide:

$$C_2H_4(g) + 3O_2(g) \rightarrow 2CO_2(g) + 2H_2O(g)$$

Ethene   Oxygen   Carbon   Water
                          Dioxide   Vapour

This water vapour condenses on cooling to form water.

∴ **Colourless gas A is ethene** and **colourless liquid B is water.**

When ethene is passed through liquid bromine an addition reaction takes place:

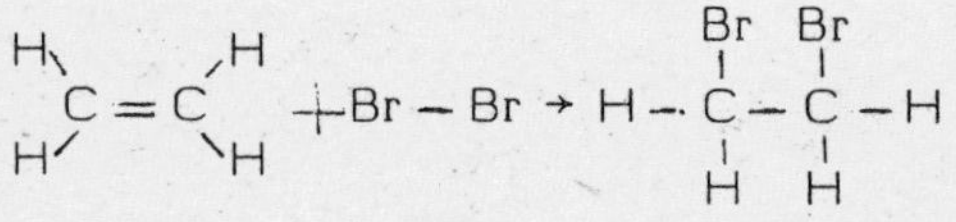

Ethene   Bromine   1,2 - Dibromoethane
                          A colourless oily liquid
                               Compound C

(b) **All ammonium salts yield ammonia on heating with an alkali.** Ammonium chloride is a white solid, ionic and soluble in water:

$$NH_4Cl(aq) + NaOH(aq) \rightarrow NaCl(aq) + H_2O(l) + NH_3(g)$$

Ammonium   Sodium   Sodium   Water   Ammonia
Chloride   Hydroxide   Chloride

$$NH_4^+(aq) + OH^-(aq) \rightarrow H_2O(l) + NH_3(g)$$

Ammonium
ion

∴ **White solid D is ammonium chloride and gas E is ammonia.**

Solutions of chlorides will give a white precipitate with silver nitrate:-

$$NH_4Cl \ (aq) + AgNO_3 \ (aq) \rightarrow NH_4NO_3 \ (aq) + AgCl \ (s)$$

Ammonium   Silver   Ammonium   Silver
Chloride   Nitrate   Nitrate   Chloride

∴ **White precipitate F is silver chloride.**

(c)   **All carbonates react with acids to form carbon di-oxide, water and salts:**

$$Na_2CO_3(s) + H_2SO_4 \ (aq) \rightarrow CO_2(g) + H_2O \ (l) + Na_2SO_4(aq)$$

Sodium   Sulphuric   Carbon   Water   Sodium
Carbonate   Acid   Dioxide   Sulphate

A white precipitate of calcium carbonate forms when carbon dioxide is passed through limewater (calcium hydroxide).

$$Ca \ (OH)_2 \ (aq) + CO_2 \ (g) \rightarrow CaCO_3 \ (s) + H_2O \ (l)$$

Calcium   Carbon   Calcium   Water
Hydroxide   Dioxide   Carbonate

∴ **Solution G is sulphuric acid and colourless gas H is carbon dioxide.**

Solutions of sulphates will give a white precipitate with barium chloride:-

$$H_2SO_4 \ (aq) + BaCl_2 \ (aq) \rightarrow BaSO_4 \ (s) + 2HCl \ (aq)$$

Sulphuric   Barium   Barium   Hydrochloric
Acid   Chloride   Sulphate   Acid

$$Ba^{2+} \ (aq) + SO_4^{2-} \ (aq) \rightarrow BaSO_4 \ (s)$$

∴ **White precipitate J is barium sulphate.**

Question 2

(a) (i) An **acid** is a substance that gives rise to H^+ ions in aqueous solution. In solutions of the same concentration (eg. 1 mol I^{-1} or M) a **strong acid** is almost completely ionised (its dissociation into ions is virtually complete), whereas a **weak acid** is only slightly ionised (partial dissociation into ions occurs).

Hydrochloric acid (HCl) is a 'strong' acid.

Ethanoic acid (CH_3COOH) is a 'weak' acid.

(ii) An **acid** provides H^+ ions or **protons** (the hydrogen ion is a proton i.e. hydrogen atom minus electron).

An **acid** is a **proton donor.**

Hydrochloric acid (HCl) **has one mole of protons per mole** and is said to be **mono protic.**

Sulphuric acid (H_2SO_4) **has two moles of protons per mole** and is said to be **diprotic.**

(b) (i) If zinc is added to a beaker containing dilute hydrochloric acid effervescence occurs as hydrogen is evolved and the zinc reacts completely.

$$Zn\ (s) + 2\ HCl\ (aq) \rightarrow ZnCl_2\ (aq) + H_2\ (g)$$

Zinc   Hydrochloric   Zinc   Hydrogen
           Acid   Chloride

i.e.

$$Zn\ (s) + 2H^+(aq) + 2Cl^-(aq) \rightarrow Zn^{2+}(aq) + 2Cl^-(aq) + H_2(g)$$

Omitting ions that are on both sides

$$Zn\ (s) + 2H^+\ (aq) \rightarrow Zn^{2+}\ (aq) + H_2\ (g)$$

The charges on both sides are now equal - this is the ionic equation.

(ii) Using a weak acid of the same concentration (eg ethanoic acid) the rate at which hydrogen is evolved is very much lower and the zinc does not react completely.

(c) **Acids react with oxides of metals** to form salts and water only:

H_2SO_4 (aq) + CuO (s) → $CuSO_4$ (aq) + H_2O (l)

Sulphuric	Copper	Copper	Water
Acid	Oxide	Sulphate	

$2H^+$ + O^{2-} → H_2O

Acids react with metal carbonates to form a salt, carbon dioxide and water:

2HCl (aq) + Na_2CO_3(s) → CO_2(g) + H_2O (l) + 2NaCl (aq)

Hydrochloric	Sodium	Carbon	Water	Sodium
Acid	Carbonate	Dioxide		Chloride

Question 3

(a) When malachite is strongly heated a colour change occurs as the **green copper carbonate starts to turn black** and moisture forms on the cooler part of the test tube. The copper carbonate decomposes on heating:

Copper (II) Carbonate (s)	→	Copper (II) Oxide (s)	+	Carbon Dioxide (g)
(Green)		(Black)		(Colourless)

The gaseous product (carbon dioxide) escapes and the substance loses mass. Particles of the substance split apart by the heat energy rearrange themselves to form a new substance (copper (II) oxide).

If the gaseous product is allowed to bubble through limewater ($Ca(OH)_2$) it will turn the limewater milky [test for CO_2].

$Ca(OH)_2$ (aq) + CO_2(g) → $CaCO_3$(s) + H_2O (l)

The moisture (water) turns blue cobalt chloride paper pink. It will also turn white anhydrous copper sulphate blue.

(b) The malachite is reacted with dilute sulphuric acid to form copper sulphate solution:

$$CuCO_3 \cdot Cu(OH)_2 \text{ (s)} + H_2SO_4 \text{(aq)} \rightarrow CO_2 \text{(g)} + H_2O \text{ (l)} + CuSO_4 \text{(aq)}$$

Malachite	Sulphuric Acid	Carbon Dioxide	Water	Copper Sulphate

When a strip of metal e.g. zinc is dipped into the copper sulphate solution for a few minutes, **a coating of pink copper metal** forms on the surface of the zinc:

$$Zn \text{ (s)} + Cu^{2+}SO_4^{2-} \text{ (aq)} \rightarrow Cu \text{ (s)} + Zn^{2+}SO_4^{2-} \text{ (aq)}$$

Atoms   Ions   Atoms   Ions

This reaction involves the transfer of electrons and is therefore a **redox** reaction. Copper is more favourable as atoms and is therefore placed lower in the reactivity series than zinc.

(c) Find the mass of porcelain 'boat'.
Find the mass of porcelain 'boat' + residue from experiment.

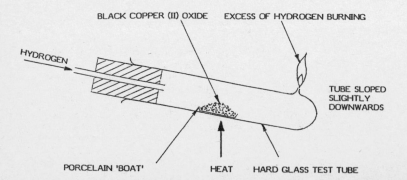

BLACK COPPER (II) OXIDE   EXCESS OF HYDROGEN BURNING

HYDROGEN

TUBE SLOPED SLIGHTLY DOWNWARDS

PORCELAIN 'BOAT'   HEAT   HARD GLASS TEST TUBE

Set up the apparatus as shown in the diagram and gently blow hydrogen gas through the apparatus. A separate sample of the gas should be collected at the outlet of the test tube and checked that when ignited it does not explode. The gas at the outlet should then be lit.

The black copper oxide is then heated until it has all turned to pink copper, i.e. glows red hot and changes to reddish-brown copper.

$$CuO \text{ (s)} + H_2 \text{ (g)} \rightarrow Cu \text{ (s)} + H_2O \text{ (g then l)}$$

(The copper oxide has been reduced by the hydrogen gas.)

When the change is complete **the heat should be removed but the hydrogen should still be passed through the apparatus** to prevent air entering and oxidising the hot copper.

After it has cooled the mass of the porcelain 'boat' plus copper is found. As a check the porcelain boat + copper could be replaced in the apparatus and the process repeated. There should be no change in mass of the porcelain 'boat' + copper, i.e. **constant mass has been achieved and reduction is complete.**

From the weighings the mass of copper can be found:
i.e.
Mass of Copper X = Mass of Boat + Copper - Mass of Boat

and the mass of oxygen can be found:

i.e.
Mass of Oxygen Y = Mass of Boat + Copper Oxide - Mass of Boat + Copper

	Copper	Oxygen
Element Mass	X	Y
Divide mass of each element by its atomic mass (to convert to moles)	$\dfrac{X}{63.5}$	$\dfrac{Y}{16}$

$$0.016 \text{ X mol} \qquad 0.063 \text{ Y mol}$$

Bring the ratio to whole numbers by dividing by the smallest. This then gives the ratio of moles of copper atoms to moles of oxygen atoms. The formula of the residue is thus determined.

Example: For the experiment with copper oxide a ratio of 80% copper to 20% oxygen is found.

$\therefore$ Mass of each element in one gram = 0.8 g copper to 0.2 g oxygen.

Converting to moles by dividing mass of each element by its atomic mass gives

$$\frac{0.8}{63.5} = 0.0125 \text{ mol} \quad \text{and} \quad \frac{0.2}{16} = 0.0125 \text{ mol}$$

In this case when brought to whole numbers **one mole of copper atoms reacts with one mole of oxygen atoms. Therefore the empirical formula of the compound is:**

$$Cu\ O$$

Question 4

(a) Pour dilute sulphuric acid into a beaker, warm gently. Add copper (II) oxide to the hot acid a little at a time. It reacts and forms a blue solution. Oxide is added until no more will react - indicating that all the acid has been neutralised. Filter off the excess copper (II) oxide and evaporate the blue filtrate in a beaker. Dip a glass rod into the hot solution and remove some of the liquid. Note if crystals form as the liquid cools. When crystals form in the test allow the hot solution in the beaker to cool. Filter off the crystals and wash them two or three times with distilled water. Dry by pressing them between two sheets of filter paper.

$$CuO\ (s) + H_2SO_4\ (aq) \rightarrow CuSO_4\ (aq) + H_2O\ (l)$$

(b) When the crystals are heated in a test tube the

blue crystals change to a **white** powder (anhydrous copper (II) sulphate), i.e. water comes off and condenses on the cooler part of the test tube.

If a few drops of water are added to the white powder the solid becomes blue and heat is given off.

$$CuSO_4 + 5H_2O \rightleftharpoons CuSO_4 . 5H_2O$$

$$\text{White} \qquad\qquad\qquad \text{Blue}$$

i.e. The copper (II) sulphate crystals contain water of crystallisation. The anhydrous copper (II) sulphate is used to indicate the presence of water.

(c) **Copper (II) Sulphate Solution**
Ions are formed by the reactions:

$$CuSO_4 \text{ (aq)} \rightarrow Cu^{2+} \text{ (aq)} + SO_4^{2-} \text{ (aq)} \qquad \text{and}$$

$$H_2O \text{ (l)} \rightleftharpoons H^+ \text{ (aq)} + OH^- \text{ (aq)}$$

At the Anode: The hydroxide ions (OH^-) are discharged in preference to the sulphate ions (SO_4^{2-}) because the hydroxide ions are higher in the electrochemical series. They give up electrons and form hydroxyl radicals which are unstable and decompose into water and oxygen, i.e. the OH radical has no independent existence and reacts immediately with three hydroxyl radicals to form water and oxygen.

$$4OH^- \text{ (aq)} \rightarrow 4OH \text{ (aq)} + 4 \text{ e}^- \qquad \text{Loss of Electrons}$$
$$| \qquad\qquad\qquad\qquad\qquad\qquad \text{(Oxidation)}$$
$$2H_2O \text{ (l)} + O_2 \text{ (g)}$$

At the Cathode: Cu^{2+} ions and H^+ ions both move there. Cu^{2+} ions are discharged in preference to hydrogen ions because copper is below hydrogen in the electro-chemical series and so the cathode becomes coated with copper.

$$2e^- + Cu^{2+} \text{ (aq)} \rightarrow Cu \text{ (s)} \qquad \text{Gain of Electrons}$$
$$\text{(Reduction)}$$

Results: Copper is deposited on the cathode; oxygen is evolved at the anode. The solution becomes acid.

The concentration of copper (II) sulphate decreases and its blue colour becomes paler. Eventually the solution becomes colourless and sulphuric acid is the electrolyte forming hydrogen and oxygen.

Question 5

(a) Oxide of lead: Pb and O

	Lead	Oxygen
Element Mass ie. 100g of oxide contains	90.8% 90.8 g	9.2% 9.2 g
Divide mass of each element by its atomic mass (to convert to moles)	$\dfrac{90.8}{207}$ = 0.439 mol	$\dfrac{9.2}{16}$ 0.575 mol
Bring the ratio to whole numbers by dividing by the smallest	$\dfrac{0.439}{0.439}$ m	$\dfrac{0.575}{0.439}$ m
$\therefore$ Ratio is :	1 m	1.31 m
or	3 m	3.93 (4) m

Therefore 3 moles of lead atoms react with 4 moles of oxygen atoms. The empirical formula of the oxide is:

Pb_3O_4 Dilead (II) Lead (IV) Oxide (Red Lead Oxide)

(b) Hydrogen Gas $\quad PbO (s) + H_2(g) \rightarrow Pb (s) + H_2O$

The experiment to determine the formula of a given mass of lead is as that for copper oxide - see question no. 3. The diagram is the same except that lead (II) oxide replaces copper (II) oxide. In the description, in place of copper (II) oxide the result of heating the lead oxide is that the yellow lead (II) oxide changes to silvery balls of molten lead:-

$PbO (s) + H_2(g) \rightarrow Pb (s) + H_2O$ (g then $\mathbf{l}$)

For the calculation: for 'copper' read 'lead', i.e.

	Lead	Oxygen
Element Mass	X	Y
Divide mass of each element by its atomic mass (to convert to moles)	$\dfrac{X}{207}$	$\dfrac{Y}{16}$
	4.83×10^{-3}	62.5×10^{-3}
	X mol	Y mol

Bring the ratio to whole numbers by dividing by the smallest. This then gives the ratio of moles of lead atoms to moles of oxygen atoms. The formula of the oxide is then determined.

Example: For the experiment with lead oxide for an amount of 2.23 g a ratio of 92.8% lead to 7.2% oxygen is found.

∴. Mass of each element in 2.23 g is 2.07 g lead and 0.16 g oxygen.

Converting to moles by dividing mass of each element by its atomic mass gives

$$\frac{2.07}{207} = \frac{1}{100} \text{ mol and } \frac{0.16}{16} = \frac{1}{100} \text{ mol}$$

i.e. $\dfrac{1}{100}$ mol of lead atoms react with $\dfrac{1}{100}$ mol oxygen atoms, or one mole of lead atoms reacts with **one mole of oxygen atoms.** **Therefore the empirical formula of the compound is**

$$PbO$$

Question 6

(a)

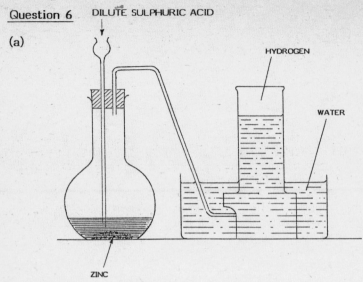

With the apparatus set up as shown in the diagram, cold, diluted sulphuric acid (1 acid : 3 water) is poured down the thistle funnel to cover the zinc. The end of the thistle funnel must be below the level of the acid to ensure that no hydrogen escapes to the atmosphere. If the action is too slow copper (II) sulphate solution may be added to speed the reaction.

$$Zn\ (s) + H_2SO_4\ (aq) \rightarrow ZnSO_4\ (aq) + H_2\ (g).$$

$$Zn\ (s) + 2H^+\ (aq) \rightarrow Zn^{2+}\ (aq) + H_2\ (g)$$

(b)

| 1 mole | 1 mole | 1 mole | 1 mole |

$$CuO\ (s) + H_2\ (g) \rightarrow Cu\ (s) + H_2O\ (l)$$

64 +16   2

80 g   2 g

ie. **80 g (1 mole) of CuO requires 2 g (1 mole) of H$_2$ to reduce it to copper.**

∴ 5 g of CuO requires $\dfrac{2}{16} = \dfrac{1}{8}$ g H$_2$ to reduce it to copper

(1/16 mole)   (1/16 mole)

As 1 mole of hydrogen = 24000 cm^3 then 1/16 mole of hydrogen = $\dfrac{24000}{16}$ = 1500 cm^3.

(c) With the apparatus set up as shown in the diagram and hydrogen supplied from the apparatus in part (a) the hydrogen produced is bubbled through an acidified solution of potassium manganate (VII) to remove any traces of hydrogen sulphide. The gas is then passed through calcium chloride U-tubes in order to remove any water vapour. When the hydrogen has had time to dispel all the air from the apparatus it is lit at the jet. The flame is allowed to burn such that hot gases from it are sucked up the funnel and through the cooled test tube by a filter pump. Part of the gases condense and form a few drops of colourless liquid.

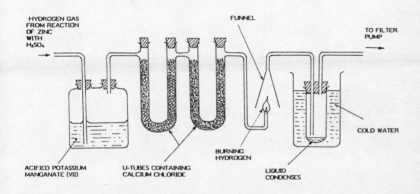

HYDROGEN GAS FROM REACTION OF ZINC WITH H₂SO₄

FUNNEL

TO FILTER PUMP

COLD WATER

ACIFIED POTASSIUM MANGANATE (VII)

U-TUBES CONTAINING CALCIUM CHLORIDE

BURNING HYDROGEN

LIQUID CONDENSES

$$2H_2 \text{ (g)} + O_2 \text{ (g)} \rightarrow 2H_2O \text{ (l)}$$

Testing the liquid for water:

(i)   Dip neutral litmus paper into it; there is no action.

(ii)   Add two drops to white anhydrous copper (II) sulphate; it turns blue.

(iii) **Find its boiling point; it is 100°C. or Find its freezing point; it is 0°C.**

(d) When a gas jar of hydrogen (the lightest gas known) is inverted over a jar of air (which is 14.5 times denser) for a few minutes the gas in both jars, when tested with a lighted splint, explodes. This indicates that hydrogen in the upper jar has spread from a region of high concentration to one of low concentration. This also applies to air in the lower jar. **This process is called diffusion.**

The molecules of the hydrogen gas are in rapid motion and readily penetrate between and become scattered among the molecules of air. Their collisions with the molecules of air frequently deflect them from their course and occasionally turn them back. It is a random process and continues until a state of equilibrium is attained. The rate of diffusion of a gas is inversely proportional to its molar mass.

Question 7

(a) (i) **An acid.** Reacts with metals to give a sulphate and hydrogen.

$$Zn(s) + H_2SO_4(aq) \rightarrow ZnSO_4(aq) + H_2(g)$$

(ii) **A dehydrating agent.** Sugar is dehydrated by concentrated sulphuric acid.

$$C_{12}H_{22}O_{11} \xrightarrow{H_2SO_4} 12C + 11H_2O$$

(iii) **An oxidising agent.** It oxidises carbon to carbon dioxide.

$$C(s) + 2H_2SO_4(Conc) \rightarrow 2H_2O(l) + CO_2(g) + 2SO_2(g)$$

and is itself reduced to sulphur dioxide.

(b) $Na\,OH(aq) + H_2SO_4(aq) \rightarrow NaHSO_4(aq) + H_2O(l)$

1 mole   1 mole   1 mole   1 mole

When evaporated the crystalline solid obtained (sodium hydrogensulphate) is known as an **acid salt** because a metal can replace the hydrogen contained in it (a solution of it in water contains H^+ ions).

If the relative volumes are changed ie. 2 moles of NaOH to one mole of H_2SO_4 then

$$2\,NaOH(aq) + H_2SO_4(aq) \rightarrow Na_2SO_4(aq) + 2\,H_2O(l)$$

2 moles   1 mole   1 mole   2 moles

When evaporated the crystalline solid (sodium sulphate) is known as a **normal salt** because it contains no hydrogen (ie. a solution of it in water contains no H^+ ions).

(c) $4\,Zn + 5\,H_2SO_4 \rightarrow 4\,ZnSO_4 + 4\,H_2O + H_2S$

4 mole   5 mole   4 mole   4 mole   1 mole

Find number of moles present in 25 cm^3 of 10 M solution.

1000 cm^3 of 10 M solution contains 10 moles.

$\therefore$ 1 cm^3 of 10 M solution contains $\dfrac{10}{1000}$ moles

and 25 cm^3 of 10 M solution contains $\dfrac{10}{1000} \times 25$ moles.

$\therefore$ 25 cm^3 of 10 M solution contains $\dfrac{1}{4}$ mole.

As 13g zinc reacts with 1/4 mole H_2SO_4

then 52g zinc reacts with 1 mole H_2SO_4

so that **260g zinc reacts with 5 mole H_2SO_4.**

From the equation: 4 moles of Zn reacts with 5 moles of H_2SO_4

therefore 260g zinc is equivalent to 4 moles

and $\frac{260}{4}$ g zinc is equal to 1 mole

ie. 65g zinc is equal to 1 mole

and as **one mole of substance is the relative atomic or molecular mass of the substance in grammes** then

the relative atomic mass of zinc = 65.

Question 8

(1) **Copper (II) Nitrate.** Cold dilute (1:1) nitric acid reacts with copper at room temperature to give copper (II) nitrate, water and nitrogen oxide. A vigorous reaction occurs as nitrogen oxide is evolved and green copper (II) nitrate forms.

$$3\,Cu(s) + 4\,HNO_3(Conc) \rightarrow Cu\,(NO_3)_2(aq) + 2H_2O(l) + 2NO_2(g)$$

(2) **Nitrogen Dioxide.** Addition of concentrated nitric acid to copper at room temperature gives nitrogen dioxide. A vigorous reaction occurs as reddish-brown nitrogen dioxide is evolved.

$$Cu(s) + 4HNO_3(Conc) \rightarrow Cu(NO_3)_2(aq) + 2H_2O(l) + 2NO_2(g)$$

(3) **Carbon Dioxide.** If fuming nitric acid is warmed with charcoal, the carbon burns and is oxidised to carbon dioxide - the nitric acid is reduced to reddish-brown nitrogen dioxide. The carbon dioxide can be collected over water, which dissolves the nitrogen dioxide.

$$C + 4HNO_3(99\%) \rightarrow CO_2(g) + 4NO_2(g) + 2H_2O(l)$$

(4) **Potassium Nitrate.** With an hydroxide which dissolves in dilute nitric acid to produce the corresponding salt and water

$$KOH(aq) + HNO_3(aq) \rightarrow KNO_3(aq) + H_2O \ (l)$$

$$OH^- + H^+ \rightarrow H_2O$$

(5) **Sulphur Dioxide.** Hot concentrated nitric acid oxidises sulphur to sulphuric acid which reacts with carbon to give SO_2:

$$S(s) + 6HNO_3(Conc) \rightarrow H_2SO_4(aq) + 2H_2O(l) + 6NO_2(g)$$
$$|$$
$$2H_2SO_4(Conc) + C(s) \rightarrow 2H_2O(l) + CO_2(g) + 2SO_2(g)$$

Question 9

(a) **(i)** Crude oil is heated (about 400°C) and is passed into a **fractionating column.** The part that is a gas at this temperature rises up the column and is steadily cooled as it rises. Different fractions of **hydrocarbons** of varying formula are obtained. After several distillations (refinings) the fractions with higher boiling points are **'cracked'** (ie. the larger **alkane** molecules are broken down into unsaturated **alkenes** which are reactive and more useful for forming other substances). For example when decane is cracked one of the possible decompositions is:

$$C_{10}H_{22} \rightarrow C_8H_{18} + C_2H_4$$

(Decane) (Octane) (Ethene)

(ii) The ethene molecule consists of two carbon atoms linked by a double bond with two hydrogen atoms attached to each carbon thus:

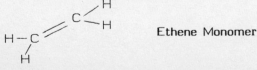

Ethene Monomer

The double bond is a reactive linkage and under the right conditions (at high temperatures and pressures in the presence of a catalyst) can be broken and reformed to join ethene molecules together into long chain-like polymers thus:

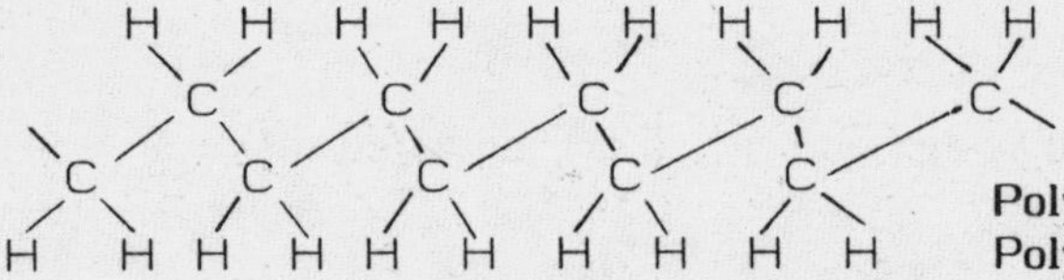

Polythene Polymer

This sort of **polymerisation** or joining together of molecules, simply by rearrangement of the inter-molecular linkage is called **addition polymerisation**. It almost always gives rise to thermoplastic molecules.

Another way of writing polymer structures is:

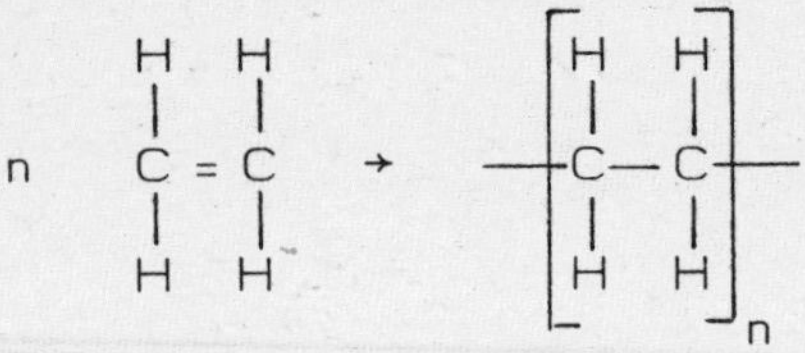

where n is a large number

Ethene   Polythene

(b)   The product is **1,2-Dibromoethane**.

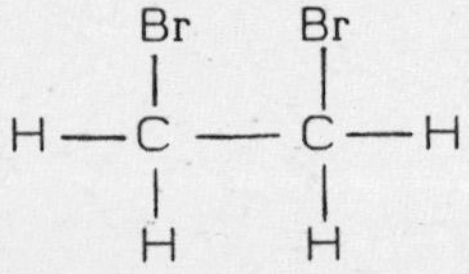

Structural Formula

When ethene was passed into bromine water the brown colour of the solution would disappear instantly.

(c) C_5H_{12}

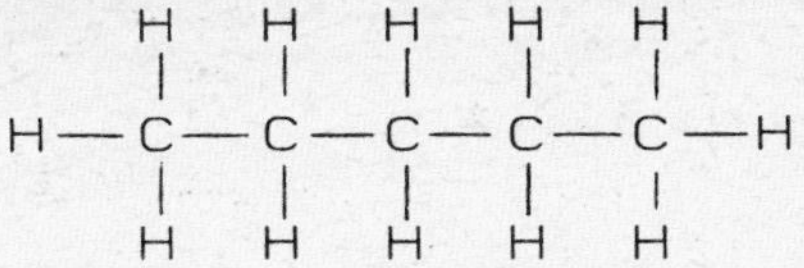

Root name: longest carbon chain: **Pentane**

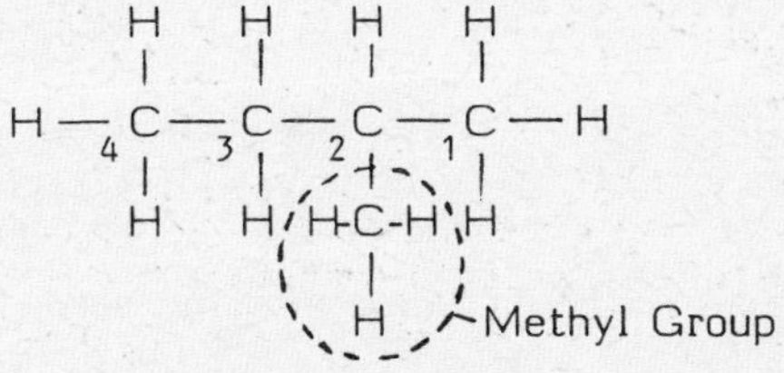

Methyl Group

Root name: longest carbon chain: Butane

2-Methylbutane

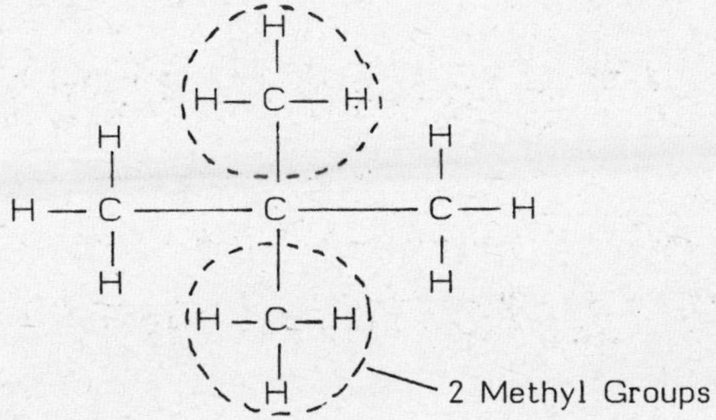

2 Methyl Groups

Root name: longest carbon chain: Propane

2,2-Dimethylpropane

(d) Relative molecular mass of ethanol C_2H_5OH

is 2 x 12 + 6 x 1   + 16

24   +   6   + 16

= 46

1 kg of water when heated through **1°C** requires 4.18 kJ

∴ 1 kg of water when heated through **70°C** requires

4.18 x 70 kJ   =   **292.6 kJ**

If 1 mole of ethanol gives 1370 kJ

then $\frac{1}{1370}$ mole of ethanol gives 1 kJ.

∴ $\frac{292.6}{1370}$ mole of ethanol gives 292.6 kJ

and as the R.A.M. of ethanol is 46 g

then $\frac{292.6}{1370}$ x 46 = 9.82 g

ie. **Minimum mass of ethanol which must be burned**

= **9.82 g**

Question 10

(a) $Na_2CO_3(s) + H_2SO_4(aq) \rightarrow Na_2SO_4(aq) + H_2O(l) + CO_2(g)$

Sodium   Sulphuric   Sodium   Water   Carbon
Carbonate   Acid   Sulphate   Dioxide

$$CO_3{}^{2-} + 2H^+ \rightarrow H_2O + CO_2$$

$CaCO_3(s) + H_2SO_4(aq) \rightarrow CaSO_4(s) + H_2O(l) + CO_2(g)$

Calcium   Sulphuric   Calcium   Water   Carbon
Carbonate   Acid   Sulphate   Dioxide

In the reaction of sodium carbonate with sulphuric acid, sodium sulphate forms, which dissolves readily in water and the reaction proceeds rapidly.

In the reaction of calcium carbonate with sulphuric acid, calcium sulphate forms around the carbonate and stops the reaction after a few seconds. Calcium sulphate is only slightly soluble in water (about 2g per litre at room temperature) and is a cause of permanent hardness in water.

(b) The **Electrochemical Series** shows which elements will displace each other from solutions of their salts.

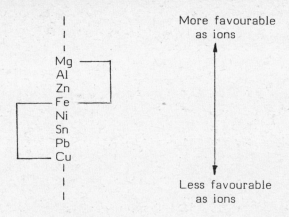

**Part of the
Electrochemical
Series**

Iron displaces copper from a solution of copper sulphate because iron is higher in the series than copper, ie. iron is more favourable as ions than copper.

$$Fe(s) + CuSO_4(aq) \rightarrow FeSO_4(aq) + Cu(s)$$

$$Fe + Cu^{2+} \rightarrow Fe^{2+} + Cu$$

Iron does not displace magnesium from a solution of magnesium sulphate because iron is lower in the series than magnesium, ie. iron is less favourable as ions than magnesium. Hence no reaction.

(c) Though both acids have the same molarity it does not mean that they have the same **strength.** The strength tells how much the molecules are ionised. A M solution of hydrochloric acid which is a 'strong' acid is almost completely dissociated into ions whereas a M solution of ethanoic acid which is a 'weak' acid is only partially dissociated into ions. The strong solution of hydrochloric acid is also a strong **electrolyte*** and is a very good conductor of electricity.

The weak solution of ethanoic acid is a weak electrolyte and is a poor conductor of electricity. Therefore for the application of the same voltage a larger current will flow through the M solution of HCl than through the M solution of CH_3CO_2H.

$$HCl(aq) \rightarrow H^+(aq) + Cl^-(aq)$$

$$CH_3CO_2H(aq) \rightleftharpoons CH_3CO_2^-(aq) + H^+(aq)$$

*Electrolyte is a compound which, when in solution or melted conducts an electric current and is decomposed by it. Some electrolytes are very good conductors of electricity because they are completely ionised.

(d) **Solutions of alkalis precipitate hydroxides of metals from solutions of their salts.**

$$FeCl_3(aq) + 3NaOH(aq) \rightarrow Fe(OH)_3(s) + 3NaCl(aq)$$

| Iron (III) Chloride | Sodium Hydroxide | Iron (III) Hydroxide | Sodium Chloride |

$$Fe^{3+}(aq) + 3OH^-(aq) \rightarrow Fe(OH)_3(s)$$

With excess alkali the precipitate $Fe(OH)_3$ remains.

$$ZnCl_2(aq) + 2NaOH(aq) \rightarrow Zn(OH)_2(s) + 2NaCl(aq)$$

| Zinc Chloride | Sodium Hydroxide | Zinc Hydroxide | Sodium Chloride |

$$Zn^{2+}(aq) + 2OH^-(aq) \rightarrow Zn(OH)_2(s)$$

Addition of the calculated quantity of alkali to a solution of a zinc salt produces a gelatinous white precipitate of zinc hydroxide $Zn(OH)_2$.

This hydroxide redissolves in excess alkali behaving as an acid in the presence of the excess alkali - it is classed as **amphoteric***.

$$ZnCl_2(aq) + 4NaOH(aq) \rightarrow Na_2Zn(OH)_4^{2-}(aq) + 2NaCl(aq)$$

| Zinc Chloride | Sodium Chloride | Sodium Zincate | Sodium Chloride |

$$Zn(OH)_2 + OH^- \rightarrow Zn(OH)_3^-$$

$$Zn(OH)_3^- + OH^- \rightarrow Zn(OH)_4^{2-}$$

Hydrated
Zinc Ion

*Amphoteric. Chemically reacting as acidic to strong bases and as basic towards strong acids.

Question 11

(a) **(i)** Manganese (IV) oxide (manganese dioxide MnO_2).

A catalyst is a substance which changes the speed of a chemical reaction but remains unchanged chemically and in mass at the end of the reaction.

(ii)

$$2 H_2O_2 (aq) \xrightarrow{\quad MnO_2 \text{ Catalyst} \quad} 2 H_2O(l) + O_2(g)$$

(iii) Put hydrogen peroxide alone and hydrogen peroxide mixed with manganese (IV) oxide into separate test tubes and place in a sand-bath. On heating the sand-bath oxygen is first to come from the mixture before the pure substance.

Add a weighed amount of manganese (IV) oxide to some hydrogen peroxide in a test tube and heat the test tube. After the reaction has ceased and the test tube has cooled add water to the test tube and re-heat. Filter off the suspension of manganese (IV) oxide, wash in warm water and dry in an oven. The mass of the filter paper and the manganese (IV) oxide is found and when the mass of the filter paper is deducted the mass of the manganese (IV) oxide is the same as before the experiment.

The foregoing experiments confirm that manganese (IV) oxide does act as a catalyst, ie. it changes the speed of the reaction and remains unchanged in mass at the end of the reaction.

(b) Hydrogen and chlorine will not combine in the dark but in sunlight the reaction is so rapid that an explosion occurs.

$$H_2(g) + Cl_2(g) \rightarrow 2\ HCl$$

Chlorine does not react with alkanes in the dark but when acted on with ultra-violet light a series of compounds are formed.

$$CH_4(g) + Cl_2(g) \rightarrow CH_3Cl(g) + HCl(g)$$
Chloromethane

and

$$CH_3Cl(g) + Cl_2(g) \rightarrow CH_2Cl_2(l) + HCl(g)$$
Dichloromethane

etc.

Bromine reacts in a similar manner.

The pulses of light set the halogen molecules vibrating until they vibrate into separate atoms. The free atoms are sufficiently reactive to attach to the alkane.

(c) Increase in pressure of a mixture of gases increases the number of reactant particles in a given volume, resulting in a higher frequency of collisions between reactant particles and therefore a higher frequency of high-energy collisions, ie. the rate of reaction is increased.

Increasing the pressure in a reaction involving gases is equivalent to increasing the concentration.

Question 12

(1) Substance J is the Halogen Iodine (I_2).

The **structure** is **molecular** crystal (covalent) because the molecules are held in place in specific positions by only comparatively weak forces. Iodine can **sublime***, it has a low melting point, does not conduct electricity and is a soft crystal.

*Sublimation is the conversion of a solid direct into vapour and subsequent condensation, without melting.

(2) Substance K is Sodium Chloride (NaCl)

The **structure** is giant **ionic** because the ions exist in large numbers in regular patterns in a crystal lattice. Any one Na^+ ion attracts around it many Cl^- ions and vice versa. Any one ion in the solid is held in a fixed position to all surrounding ions by strong ionic bonds. When molten or dissolved in water it is a good conductor of electricity because the ions are free to move.

(3) Substance L is Magnesium (Mg)

The **structure** is a **metallic** lattice. Valency electrons can move freely through the lattice even though the atoms are packed tightly together. This accounts for the fact that it is a good conductor of electricity. Metal lattices are strong with high melting and boiling points. It reacts slowly with water because a film of hydroxide prevents further action. It displaces hydrogen from dilute acids, and even from very dilute nitric acid.

(4) Substance M is Carbon (C) - Graphite

The **structure** is giant covalent **(macromolecular)**. Each carbon atom is bonded covalently to three others in a giant flat array. The fourth electron is delocalised (spread out) over the whole plane of carbon atoms. The giant planes are held only loosely to each other by secondary bonding. It is the only non-metal to conduct electricity with ease. Carbon burns steadily in air to form CO_2.

(5) Substance N is Hydrogen Chloride Gas.

The **structure** is covalent **(molecular)**. It is not a conductor but it forms a conducting solution with water ie. hydrochloric acid. This acid is a strong electrolyte and has an ionic structure which conducts electricity very well and turns litmus red.

Question 13

(a) The industrial electrolysis of brine (aqueous sodium chloride) is carried out using the mercury cell or the diaphragm cell. The total energy requirement for either process is virtually the same.

The mercury cell has a mercury cathode which flows steadily throughout the process, whilst the anode is made of carbon (graphite).

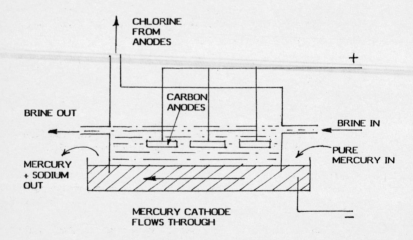

At the cathode: Both Na^+ and H^+ ions move there but **Na^+ ions are preferentially discharged** even though they are higher in the electrochemical series:

$$2Na^+(aq) + 2e \rightarrow 2Na(s)$$

The sodium dissolves in the mercury forming an amalgam.   The amalgam is pumped into another container where water is added to produce aqueous sodium chloride and hydrogen gas:

$$2Na \text{ (amalgam)} + 2H_2O(l) \rightarrow \underbrace{2Na^+(aq) + 2OH^-(aq)}_{\text{Sodium Hydroxide (aq)}} + H_2(g)$$

The mercury is recycled through the cell and the sodium hydroxide is evaporated to dryness, the molten substance solidifies as sticks or pellets.   The hydrogen is collected or converted into synthetic hydrogen chloride by burning it with chlorine.

At the anode: The anode being made of carbon is not attacked by chlorine.   Both Cl^- and OH^- ions move there, but **Cl^- ions are preferentially discharged** even though they are higher in the electrochemical series.

$$2\,Cl^-(aq) \rightarrow Cl_2(g) + 2e$$

The chlorine is dried, liquefied and stored.

(b)   The products of the electrolysis are **Hydrogen Gas (H_2), Chlorine Gas (Cl_2)** and **Sodium Hydroxide (NaOH).**

Hydrogen is used in the manufacture of ammonia (Haber process) and in the hydrogenation (hardening of oils).

Chlorine is used in the manufacture of hydrochloric acid (hydrogen is burned in chlorine) and also in the manufacture of plastics.

Sodium hydroxide is used in the manufacture of soap and also in paper making.

Question 13 (cont'd)

Alternative

(a) **The diaphragm cell** has two compartments separated by a porous membrane (asbestos). The anode is contained in one compartment and the cathode in the other. The anode is made of titanium and the cathode is made of steel.

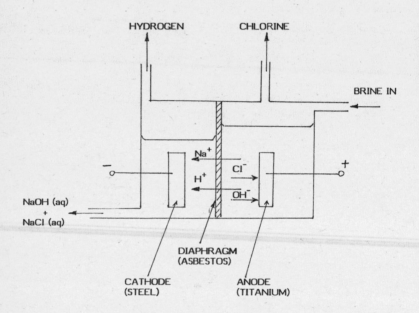

HYDROGEN

CHLORINE

BRINE IN

Na⁺

Cl⁻

H⁺

OH⁻

NaOH (aq)
+
NaCl (aq)

DIAPHRAGM
(ASBESTOS)

CATHODE
(STEEL)

ANODE
(TITANIUM)

The brine sprayed in percolates out through the asbestos diaphragm and is partly electrolysed before draining to the base of the vessel.

At the cathode: hydrogen is evolved $2H^+ + 2e^- \rightarrow H_2(g)$ leaving OH^- hence more water ionises.

At the anode: chlorine is evolved $2Cl^-(aq) - 2e^- \rightarrow Cl_2(g)$ The diaphragm keeps the chlorine away from the products at the cathode and enables the cathode section to be drained.

The 'catholyte' (the solution draining from the cathode, in this case sodium hydroxide and sodium chloride) is separated until it contains 50% NaOH in which NaCl is almost insoluble and so it is precipitated.

The products of the electrolysis are as for the mercury cell process ie. **hydrogen, chlorine** and **sodium hydroxide**.

Question 14

(a) (1)

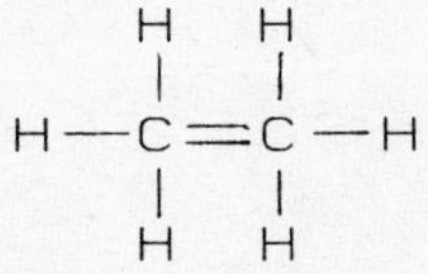

```
    H   H
    |   |
H — C = C — H
    |   |
    H   H
```

Ethene (C_2H_4)

A gas

(2) $O = C = O$

Carbon Dioxide (CO_2)

A gas

(3)

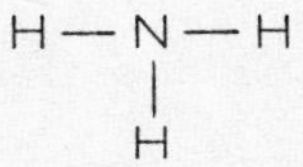

```
H — N — H
    |
    H
```

Ammonia (NH_3)

A gas

(4) $H — O — H$

Water (H_2O)

A liquid

(b)

	Ionic	**Covalent**
eg	Sodium Chloride (Na+Cl-)	eg Water (H_2O)
(1)	Crystalline solid.	Liquid or gas.
(2)	Consists of ions.	Consists of molecules.
(3)	Electrolytes (Conduct electricity when melted or dissolved)	Non-electrolytes (Do not conduct electricity)
(4)	High melting point and boiling point (non-volatile)	Low melting point and boiling point (volatile)

(c) The sodium chloride crystal contains an equal number of sodium atoms and chlorine atoms but they do not form molecules. The crystal is built up of sodium ions Na^+ and chloride ions Cl^- rather than neutral atoms or molecules. As the entire crystal is electrically neutral the numbers of Na^+ and Cl^- ions must be equal. The electrical attraction between positive and negative ions accounts for the binding in the ionic solid.

The ions in the crystal are arranged in layers in which a Cl^- ion lies in front of each Na^+ ion and a Cl^- ion lies behind each Na^+ ion. Each ion is surrounded by six oppositely charged ions in an arrangement called a lattice. Because of the proximity of the oppositely charged ions in the lattice the inter-atomic forces are at their maximum and therefore it forms a strongly bonded, stable structure.

(d) When metals (**electropositive**) bond with non-metals (**electronegative**) ionic compounds are formed. In sodium (large atoms) metallic bonding is weak. In magnesium (smaller atoms) metallic bonding is stronger. The strength of metallic bonding is related to the size of metal atoms - small atoms pack together closely to form strong bonded structures with high melting points. Metal bond strength is also related to the number of **delocalised** outer electrons.

Magnesium metal is a group 2 metal, its atoms are smaller and less electropositive than those of sodium (group 1) ie. since the atoms of group 2 metals are smaller than group 1 they form stronger bonds. The oxide of magnesium has greater stability (or low energy), it is an ionic compound whose great stability can be attributed to strong electrostatic forces between the small positively charged Mg^{2+} ions and the negatively charged oxide ions O^{2-}. The fact that the Mg^{2+} ions are very small allows these positive ions to approach closely to the negative oxide ions resulting in strong attractive forces, hence MgO has a much higher melting point than NaCl.

Mg melts at 650°C   MgO melts at 2800°C

Na melts at 98°C   NaCl melts at 801°C

(e) Diamond is a naturally occurring form of pure crystal-line carbon. Each carbon atom is surrounded by four others arranged tetrahedrally. The result is a compact structural network bound by normal chemical bonds and comprises the familiar diamond shape. It forms a giant covalent array. To .push it out of position would require the distortion of many strong and pre-cisely positioned carbon to carbon bonds.

Diamond therefore is one of the hardest substances known and has a very high melting point because of the large amount of energy required to break the vast number of covalent bonds.

Electropositivity is the tendency of an atom to lose electrons.

Electronegativity is the tendency of an atom to pull electrons towards it.

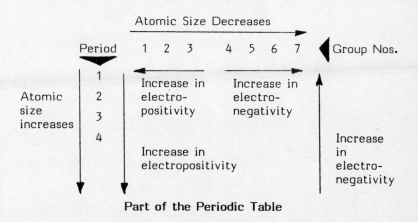

Part of the Periodic Table

Delocalisation means a 'spreading out' of electrons.

Question 15

(a) Our atmosphere is largely transparent to solar radiation. As this radiation strikes the earth it becomes heat. Some of the heat is radiated from the ground back into the atmosphere as infrared radiation, but it does not pass out into space again. The carbon dioxide and water vapour in the atmosphere absorb this energy, trap it and re-emit it back to earth. This is called the **'greenhouse effect'** because energy from the sun passes easily through the glass into a greenhouse but, when re-radiated, is absorbed by the moist air within. The energy is trapped. An increase in the Co^2 concentration means more infra-red radiation is trapped and re-emitted back to the earth producing a build up of infra-red radiation in the atmosphere and a mean global temperature rise. The concentration of CO^2 in the atmosphere is increasing, the principal source being the consumption of transport fuels. If the amount of CO^2 in the atmosphere changed from time, the amount of heat energy that the earth received and retained would change too. Possibly during some periods of the earth's history there has been a greater production of CO^2 than at other periods. Then, due to the greenhouse effect, the earth would be warmer and a period of melting glaciers would occur. Conversely with reduced CO^2 production the earth would be colder and an 'ice age' would ensue.

(b) The burning of petrol in car engines adds **lead compounds to the atmosphere.** Petrol contains tetra-ethyl lead (IV), $Pb\ (C_2H_5)_4$ and most airborne lead is produced from this compound. It can cause depression, irritability, brain damage and even death. Lead is the most dangerous airborne pollutant because it accumulates in the body (Pb^{2+} replaces Ca^{2+} in bones) and is the cause of much illness and damage to the central nervous system and brain. There is serious concern about this pollution particularly in cities and in the U.S.A. the use of lead-free petrol is being enforced.

(c) **Acid rain** is produced by the dissolving of sulphur dioxide (SO_2) in water to give H_2SO_3 and subsequently H_2SO_4 . Sulphur dioxide is produced when sulphur or sulphur containing substances are burned in oxygen:

$$S + O_2 \rightarrow SO_2 \text{ (g)}$$

The oxide is acidic and with water gives sulphurous and sulphuric acids

$$SO_2 + H_2O \rightarrow H_2SO_3 \rightleftharpoons 2H^+ + SO_3^{2-}$$
$$\text{Sulphurous Acid}$$

$$SO_3 + H_2O \rightarrow H_2SO_4 \rightleftharpoons 2H^+ + SO_4^{2-}$$
$$\text{Sulphuric Acid}$$

The sources of SO_2 are:	Total SO_2 discharged into atmosphere
Coal combustion	70%
Oil combustion and refining	20%
Cu, Zn, Pb smelting and other	10%

Relatively pure rain water has a pH around 5.5 - 5.7 but owing to SO_2 emissions the pH of rain can drop as low as 2. This increases the acidity of waterways, in particular - lakes. In addition to increasing acidity of lakes and affecting aquatic life, acid rain accelerates the leaching of nutrients from soils, affects the metabolism of soil organisms, increases metallic corrosion and the destruction of basic building materials such as limestone and marble. Sulphur dioxide in association with particulate materials and at high humidities can have serious effect on human beings, plants and materials.

(d) **Contamination of water by fertilizers** leads to very undesirable effects. This contamination results largely from the phosphate (PO_4^{3-}) and nitrate (NO_3^-) present in fertilizers. Fertilizers are made from simple chemicals, such as ammonium nitrate, NH_4NO_3, that are quite soluble in water. During and after a hard rain the surface run-off carries much of the fertilizer away to waterways, rivers etc. In waters that contain excessive amounts of phosphate and nitrate leached from feretilized farm land algae growths are some-times so great they tend to choke out desirable life forms. The algae growth may lead to eutrophication ie. an oxygen deficient environment is produced and so plant and fish life are adversely affected.

It is certain that nitrate in sufficient concentration is toxic to most higher organisms. It is thought that nitrates may cause cancer of the stomach and also be especially dangerous to infants who are abnormally susceptible to poisoning via nitrate in their drinking water. Natural fertilizers are not water-soluble but release nitrate, phosphate and metal ions at a rate commensurate with the rate of uptake by the plants. Fertilizer products now on the market imitate nature in releasing their nutrients at a slower rate.

Question 16

(a) Starch solution is made from wheat/barley/potatoes etc. ie. mashed with hot water and heated with malt at 50°C for about an hour. The starch is **hydrolysed** to **maltose** by the **enzyme diastase** contained in the malt:

$$(C_6H_{10}O_5)_n \text{ (s)} + \frac{n}{2} H_2O \text{ (l)} \xrightarrow{\text{Diastase}} \frac{n}{2} C_{12}H_{22}O_{11} \text{(aq)}$$

(Maltose)

On cooling to 30°C the mixture is fermented with yeast for a few days. The **maltose** is converted into **glucose** by the **enzyme maltase** contained in the yeast and the glucose is converted into **ethanol** by the **enzyme zymase**, also contained in the yeast:

$$C_{12}H_{22}O_{11} \text{(aq)} + H_2O \text{(l)} \xrightarrow{\text{Maltase}} 2C_6H_{12}O_6 \text{(aq)}$$

(Maltose)   (Glucose)

$$C_6H_{12}O_6 \text{(aq)} \rightarrow 2C_2H_5OH \text{(aq)} + 2CO_2 \text{(g)}$$

(Glucose)   (Ethanol)

The yeast is killed when the proportion of ethanol reaches about 15%, so that any further concentration of the solution has to be carried out by distillation. Even then the ethanol is not pure (maximum concentration about 96%) and special methods are required to remove the last traces of water.

(b) Crude oil, comprising many alkanes, is heated and passed into a fractionating column. Various fractions of alkanes of differing chain length are obtained. These fractions are redistilled and the longer chain alkanes (vaporised fractions) are converted into shorter chain ones by a process known as 'cracking'. The vaporised fractions together with steam are passed, at a moderate temperature, through a fluidised bed of alumina (Al_2O_3) and silica (SiO_2) which acts as a catalyst. The products of this 'cracking' process are smaller molecule alkanes and alkenes, which are then separated into several fractions by a fractionating column. The alkene ethene which is produced is a starting point for the production of ethanol. Ethanol is made by reacting ethene with steam at about 300°C and about seventy times atmospheric pressure using a catalyst of phosphoric acid:

$$C_2H_4(g) + H_2O(g) \xrightleftharpoons[H_3PO_4]{\text{Phosphoric Acid}} C_2H_5OH(g)$$

Direct hydration method.

(c) Relative molecular mass 32 = 100% i.e. 1% = 0.32

$\therefore$ 37.5% = Carbon = 37.5 x 0.32 = 12

50.0% = Oxygen = 50.0 x 0.32 = 16

12.5% = Hydrogen = 12.5 x 0.32 = 4

Divide by relative atomic mass of each element:

Carbon = $\frac{12}{12}$; Oxygen = $\frac{16}{16}$; Hydrogen = $\frac{4}{1}$

$\therefore$ Carbon 1 mole; Oxygen 1 mole; Hydrogen 4 moles

$\therefore$ Molecular formula = COH_4

Alcohol Series = $Cn\ H_{2n+1}\ OH$ simplest **homologous**
series

with $n = 1 = C\ H_3\ OH$

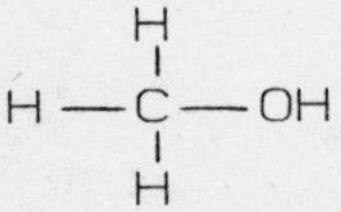

$$H - \overset{\overset{\displaystyle H}{|}}{\underset{\underset{\displaystyle H}{|}}{C}} - OH \quad = \quad \textbf{Methanol}$$

ie. hydrogen atom removed from methane and replaced
by an -OH

Methane CH_4 $\quad\quad H - \overset{\overset{\displaystyle H}{|}}{\underset{\underset{\displaystyle H}{|}}{C}} - H$

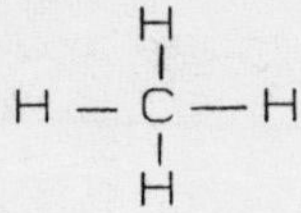

Question 17

(a) **Method 1. Action of an acid on a metal**

eg. $Zn(s) + H_2SO_4(aq) \rightarrow ZnSO_4(aq) + H_2(g)$

Hydrogen gas is evolved.

**Method 2. Action of an acid on an insoluble oxide or
hydroxide**

eg. $CuO(s) + H_2SO_4(aq) \rightarrow CuSO_4(aq) + H_2O(l)$

Water is formed.

Method 3. Action of an acid on an insoluble carbonate

eg. $PbCO_3(s) + 2HNO_3(aq) \rightarrow Pb(NO_3)_2(aq) + CO_2 + H_2O$

Carbon dioxide gas is evolved.

(b) (i) **Action of an acid on an insoluble oxide.
Magnesium sulphate from magnesium oxide and
sulphuric acid.**

Pour diluted sulphuric acid into a beaker and warm
gently (it should not be boiled). Add magnesium oxide

a little at a time. It reacts without effervescence. Continue to acid oxide until no more reacts, showing that all the acid has been neutralised.

Filter off excess magnesium oxide. Evaporate the filtrate in a beaker and test now and then to find if it will form crystals when it cools.

When crystals form in the test, let the solution in the beaker cool. Cover beaker and leave for a few hours. Good crystals form slowly. Filter off the crystals, wash them with a little cold distilled water and dry by pressing gently between two pieces of filter paper.

$$MgO \text{ (s)} + H_2SO_4(aq) \rightarrow MgSO_4(aq) + H_2O(l)$$

(ii) To prepare an insoluble salt from a soluble salt. Magnesium carbonate from magnesium sulphate.

Mix together solutions of two soluble salts each containing half of the required salt. The required insoluble salt is then precipitated.

$$MgSO_4(aq) + 2NaHCO_3(aq) \rightarrow Na_2SO_4 + Mg(HCO_3)_2(aq)$$

	Sodium	Magnesium
	Hydrogencarbonate	Hydrogen-carbonate

$$Mg(HCO_3)_2(aq) \underset{warmed}{\rightarrow} MgCO_3(s) + H_2O(l) + CO_2(g)$$

Filter off the precipitate, wash it with distilled water and dry thoroughly.

(c) (i) Sulphate ion is detected by the white precipitate it gives on the addition of barium chloride solution in the presence of dilute hydrochloric acid.

$$MgSO_4(aq) + BaCl_2(aq) \rightarrow BaSO_4(s) + MgCl_2(aq)$$

(ii) A carbonate forms carbon dioxide which turns calcium hydroxide solution milky. Add dilute hydrochloric acid and pass the gas evolved through calcium hydroxide solution which turns milky.

$$MgCO_3(s) + 2HCl(aq) \rightarrow MgCl_2(aq) + H_2O(l) + CO_2(g)$$

Question 18

(a) Consider (i) carbon dioxide, (ii) water vapour, (iii) oxygen.

(i) Carbon dioxide: When air is passed through limewater ($Ca(OH)_2$ (aq)) for some time, a precipitate (calcium carbonate) forms. This is the standard test for carbon dioxide.

Or slowly pump a known volume of dry air through potassium hydroxide - carbon dioxide is completely absorbed by potassium hydroxide:

$$2KOH(s) + CO_2(g) \rightarrow K_2CO_3(s) + H_2O(l)$$

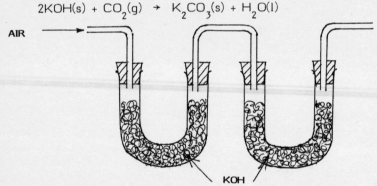

AIR

KOH

The increase in the weight of the tubes gives the weight of carbon dioxide in the volume of air.

(ii) Water vapour: When calcium chloride is left in the atmosphere for a long time (three or four days) it absorbs water vapour to such an extent that it dissolves in it. It is said to be deliquescent.

Or pump a known volume of air through anhydrous calcium chloride. The solid takes up water to form the hydrated salt $CaCl_2 \cdot 6H_2O$.

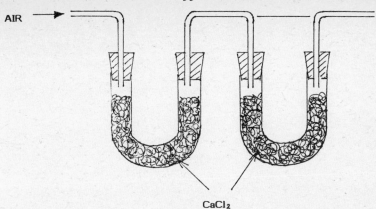

AIR ⟶

CaCl₂

The increase in the weight of the tubes gives the weight of water in this volume of air. Air contains between 0 to 6% water vapour.

(iii) Oxygen: When a candle is placed in a bell-jar of air over water the candle will burn as long as oxygen is present. When all the oxygen is used up the candle goes out. Candle wax contains carbon and hydrogen only and when it burns the oxygen from the air reacts with the hydrogen and carbon to give:

$$C + O_2 \rightarrow CO_2 ; \ 2H + O_2 \rightarrow 2H_2O$$

These reactions cease when the oxygen has been used up and the flame is extinguished.

Or pass a known volume of air over heated copper until no further change is observed (ie. reddish-brown copper turns black as the oxide is formed). The volume of trapped air can be seen to decrease:

$$2 \, Cu(s) + O_2(g) \rightarrow 2 \, Cu \, O(s)$$

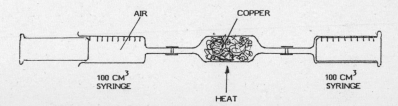

AIR   COPPER

100 CM³   100 CM³
SYRINGE   SYRINGE

HEAT

Note the volume of the gas remaining when the heating has stopped and the apparatus is cool (about 30 cm³ should remain, ie. 1/5 has been used up). Test small samples of the gas in the syringe - it extinguishes a lighted splint (ie. no oxygen in the gas and also if a few drops of calcium hydroxide are mixed with the gas it does not go milky (ie. no carbon dioxide contained in the gas).

(b) **(i) Oxygen.** The manufacture of sulphuric acid by the **'contact' process** uses air as a raw material. The first step in the process is burning sulphur in air, ie. the **oxygen gas** from the air is used:

$$S(s) + O_2(g) \rightarrow SO_2(g)$$

The sulphur dioxide is then mixed with a large excess of air. The dust is removed, it is washed with water and then dried by bubbling through concentrated sulphuric acid. This process is carried out because the purified air/sulphur dioxide mixture is passed over a catalyst (vanadium (V) oxide) which could be poisoned by impurities. The mixture is pumped through a heat exchanger where it is heated to 500°C.

In the reaction chamber sulphur trioxide is formed on the large surface of the catalyst:

$$2SO_2(g) + O_2 \rightarrow 2SO_3(g)$$

Sulphur trioxide added directly to water produces sulphuric acid as a fine mist, so that in practice the gas is dissolved in concentrated sulphuric acid to give oleum $(H_2S_2O_7)$.

$$H_2SO_4(g) + SO_3(g) \rightarrow H_2S_2O_7(l)$$

The oleum is then diluted to produce sulphuric acid (H_2SO_4).

$$H_2S_2O_7(l) + H_2O(l) \rightarrow 2 H_2SO_4(l)$$

(ii) Nitrogen. Nitrogen gas is separated from air by the fractional distillation of liquid air and the bulk of the **nitrogen gas** is used by the **Haber process** in the preparation of ammonia (NH_3).

Nitrogen and hydrogen (from the cracking of crude oil) are mixed in the ratio 1:3. The mixture is compressed to 250 atmospheres (the high pressure improves the yield and the rate of production of ammonia). The gases are passed through a heat exchanger and are heated to 500°C. In the reaction chamber ammonia is formed on the large surface of the catalyst which is made of finely divided iron. About 10% of the gases combine to produce ammonia:

$$N_2(g) + 3H_2(g) \rightleftharpoons 2NH_3(g)$$

Exothermic
Reaction

Question 19

(i) **Ethene** (C_2H_4) is a colourless gas which burns in air with a faintly luminous flame:

$$C_2H_4(g) + 3O_2(g) \rightarrow 2CO_2(g) + 2H_2O(l)$$

When added to a solution of bromine water the alkene causes the bromine water to decolourise.

Ethene   Bromine   1,2-Dibromoethane

The brown colour disappears quickly.

F is Ethene.

(ii) **Ethanoic Acid** (CH_3CO_2H) is a colourless liquid. It reacts with sodium hydrogencarbonate to give CO_2.

$$NaHCO_3(s) + CH_3CO_2H(l) \rightarrow H_2O(l) + CO_2(g) + CH_3CO_2Na(aq)$$

| Sodium Hydrogen- carbonate | Ethanoic Acid | | Sodium Ethanoate $(Na^+ + CH_3CO_2^-)$ |

$$CO_2(g) + Ca(OH)_2 (aq) \rightarrow CaCO_3(s) + H_2O(l)$$

      Limewater   Milky PPT

Ethanoic acid reacts with magnesium to give hydrogen:

$$Mg(s) + 2 CH_3CO_2H(aq) \rightarrow Zn(CH_3CO_2)_2(aq) + H_2(g)$$

        Ethanoic Acid   Zinc Ethanoate

$$(Zn^{2+} + 2(CH_3CO_2)^-)$$

G is Ethanoic Acid.
H is Hydrogen.
J is Carbon Dioxide.

(iii) **Ethanol** (C_2H_5OH) is a colourless liquid which burns in air:

$$C_2H_5OH(l) + 3O_2(g) \rightarrow 2CO_2(g) + 3H_2O(l) + Heat$$

It reacts with sodium to produce hydrogen:

$$2C_2H_5OH(l) + 2Na(s) \rightarrow 2C_2H_5ONa(l) + H_2(g)$$
Ethanol   Sodium Ethoxide

K is Ethanol.

Ethanol can be converted to ethene by dehydration (removal of the elements of water) using excess concentrated sulphuric acid at 160°C:

$$C_2H_5OH(l) + H_2SO_4(l) \rightleftharpoons C_2H_5HSO_4(l) + H_2O(l)$$
$$|$$
$$C_2H_4(g) + H_2SO_4(l)$$

$$\therefore\ C_2H_5OH(l) \rightarrow C_2H_4(g) + H_2O(l)$$
    Ethanol   Ethene

Ethanol can be converted to ethanoic acid by oxidation:

$$C_2H_5OH(l) + O_2(g) \rightarrow CH_3CO_2H(aq) + H_2O(l)$$
Ethanol   Oxygen   Ethanoic acid
            from the
            air

Question 20

(a)

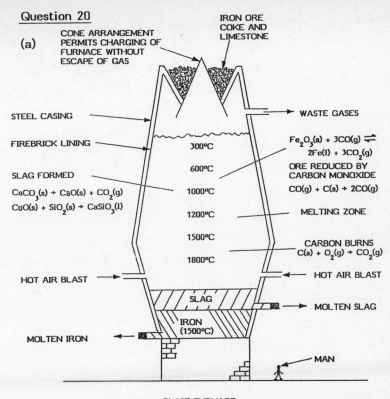

CONE ARRANGEMENT PERMITS CHARGING OF FURNACE WITHOUT ESCAPE OF GAS

IRON ORE COKE AND LIMESTONE

STEEL CASING

FIREBRICK LINING

SLAG FORMED

$CaCO_3(s) \to CaO(s) + CO_2(g)$

$CaO(s) + SiO_2(s) \to CaSiO_3(l)$

300°C
600°C
1000°C
1200°C
1500°C
1800°C

WASTE GASES

$Fe_2O_3(s) + 3CO(g) \rightleftharpoons 2Fe(l) + 3CO_2(g)$

ORE REDUCED BY CARBON MONOXIDE

$CO(g) + C(s) \to 2CO(g)$

MELTING ZONE

CARBON BURNS
$C(s) + O_2(g) \to CO_2(g)$

HOT AIR BLAST

HOT AIR BLAST

SLAG

IRON (1500°C)

MOLTEN IRON

MOLTEN SLAG

MAN

BLAST FURNACE

The iron ore is mixed with coke and limestone (to remove earthy impurities) and dropped into the furnace. Hot air at 800°C is blown in near to the base of the furnace through jets at supersonic speeds and as the air moves upwards the charge moves downwards.

(iii)

The coke burns in the air forming carbon dioxide and producing temperatures up to 1800°C. Further up the furnace the dioxide is reduced to monoxide:

$C(s) + O_2(g) \to CO_2(g)$ Exothermic reaction

$CO_2(g) + C(s) \to 2CO(g)$

(i)

The carbon monoxide reduces the iron oxide (Fe_2O_3) to molten iron which runs down to the bottom of the furnace.

The reactions are reversible and excess carbon monoxide is necessary to reduce the oxide completely

$$Fe_2O_3(s) + 3CO(g) \rightleftharpoons 2Fe(l) + 3CO_2(g)$$

The gases* leaving the furnace contain about 25% of carbon monoxide.

(ii)

The limestone decomposes into calcium oxide. This combines with sand (silicon (IV) oxide, SiO_2) present as an impurity in the ore and forms a slag of calcium silicate

$$CaCO_3(s) \rightarrow CaO(s) + CO_2(g)$$

$$CaO(s) + SiO_2(s) \rightarrow CaSiO_3(l)$$

The slag** is run out of the furnace and is processed for use in industry.

The iron absorbs carbon as it moves down the furnace and this lowers its melting point. Both iron and slag are molten and drop to the bottom of the furnace. The less dense slag floats on top of the iron and prevents oxidation of the iron by the air blast.

The iron and the slag are run out of separate holes from time to time. The process is continuous.

For reasons of economy the excess heat energy and any by-products are utilised in the extraction process itself.

In modern furnaces, fuel oil mixed with the hot air replaces the coke. Since the oil cools the mixture, oxygen is added to the air blast to maintain the 1800ºC temperature.

(iii)

* The hot exhaust gases from the furnace are passed through separators wherein the dust is extracted. The dust which contains small particles of coke and iron ore etc. is made into

pellets and returned to the furnace. The gases are used to heat the ingoing air blast or are utilised in the generation of power.

** Slag containing a considerable amount of calcium phosphate is processed and sold as a fertiliser whilst slag having little calcium phosphate is processed and sold as building material.

(b) Two differences in composition between pig iron and steel. Pig iron is an exceptionally hard brittle metal containing about 4/5% carbon. The uncombined impurities cause defects in the crystal lattice.

Steel is produced by first removing carbon and other impurities from the molten pig iron by blowing through hot air (Bessemer process) or pure oxygen (Linz Donawitz process). Precise quantities of carbon are added to the pure iron (from 0.1% in mild steels to 1.5% in hard steels). Other metals (transition) are added to vary the properties of the metal.

(c)

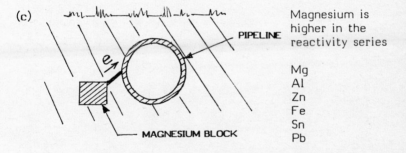

PIPELINE

MAGNESIUM BLOCK

Magnesium is higher in the reactivity series

Mg
Al
Zn
Fe
Sn
Pb

The reactive metal (Mg) corrodes and passes electrons to the pipe making it difficult for iron ions to escape and for rusting to take place.

The Mg is 'sacrificed' to project the iron.

$$Mg - 2e \rightarrow Mg^{2+} \quad \text{(Mg corroding)}$$

$$Fe^{2+} + 2e \rightarrow Fe \quad \text{(Iron is prevented from rusting)}$$

(d) Cans used in foodstuffs need protection against acids in fruit juices and foods and the metal used to plate the cans is tin. This affords good protection, but if the tin layer is broken then rusting sets in rapidly because tin is below iron in the reactivity series. Tin has its own protective layer of tin oxide which keeps the plating in good condition.

Question 21

(a) **Sulphite ions to sulphur dioxide molecules.**

Starting materials: sodium sulphite and dilute hydrochloric acid.
Add dilute hydrochloric acid to sodium sulphate and heat. All sulphites react with dilute acids to produce sulphur dioxide:

$$Na_2SO_3^{2-} (s) + 2H^+Cl(aq) \rightarrow 2NaCl(aq) + H_2O(l) + SO_2(g)$$

Test the gas produced (SO_2) with potassium dichromate (VI) paper, moistened. This orange paper reacts to form green chromium (III) ions, ie. paper turns from orange to green in the presence of SO_2. N.B. Experiments should be performed in a fume cupboard because sulphur dioxide is a poisonous gas.

(b) **Ammonium ions to ammonia molecules.**

Starting materials: ammonium chloride and calcium hydroxide.
Mix the ammonium chloride and calcium hydroxide in a test tube. Apply heat to the closed end of the tube and collect the ammonia gas by downward displacement.

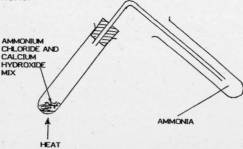

AMMONIUM CHLORIDE AND CALCIUM HYDROXIDE MIX

AMMONIA

HEAT

$$2NH_4Cl(s) + Ca(OH)_2(s) \rightarrow CaCl_2(s) + 2H_2O(l) + 2NH_3(g)$$

$$NH_4^+(s) + HO^-(s) \rightarrow H_2O(l) + NH_3(g)$$

Test the gas produced (NH_3) by dipping a glass rod into concentrated HCl and holding it in the ammonia fumes. Dense white fumes of ammonium chloride are formed:

$$NH_3(g) + HCl(g) \rightarrow NH_4Cl(s)$$

Ammonia also turns moist red litmus paper blue.

(c) Hydrogen ions to hydrogen molecules.

Starting materials: zinc metal and dilute hydrochloric acid.
Experiments suggest that hydrogen ions (H^+) are too reactive to exist without the presence of water and therefore that acidity can only occur in the presence of water.

When zinc reacts with an acid it dissolves in it and hydrogen gas is evolved:

$$Zn(s) + 2HCl(aq) \rightarrow ZnCl_2(aq) + H_2(g)$$

bubbles from it

$$Zn^- + 2H^+Cl^- \rightarrow Zn^{2+}Cl_2^- + H_2$$

The negative ions (anions) eg. Cl^- take no part in the reaction. Hydrogen ions have gained electrons – hydrogen ions have been reduced. Hydrogen ions have become hydrogen atoms. Hydrogen atoms combine to form hydrogen molecules (H_2).

Test the gas produced by holding a lighted splint to it. A loud squeak or 'pop' is heard as the gas explodes with oxygen from the air to give water.

(d) Chlorine molecules to chloride ions.

If chlorine gas is bubbled through water chlorine water is obtained. Chlorine may be prepared from a mixture of sodium chloride, sodium hydrogensulphate and potassium manganese (VII) in the ratio by mass of 3:6:1. Mix the reagents well in a mortar. Place in a test tube. Gentle heating causes the evolution of chlorine.

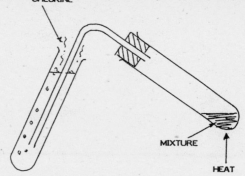

Bubble the chlorine through water. It is fairly soluble in water forming yellowish chlorine water.

$$H_2O + Cl_2(g) \rightleftharpoons HCl(aq) + HClO(aq)$$
hypochlorous acid

The greenish yellow chlorine gas turns damp blue litmus red, then bleaches it.

The chloride ion in solution is detected by the white precipitate it gives on addition of silver nitrate solution:

$$Ag^+(aq) + Cl^-(aq) \rightarrow AgCl(s)$$

N.B. Experiments should be performed in a fume cupboard because chlorine is a poisonous gas.

Question 22

(a) When the alcohol ethanol (C_2H_5OH) reacts with the acid ethanoic acid (CH_3CO_2H) a new compound is produced:

$$H-C-C-OH + C-C-H \rightarrow H-C-C-O-C-C-H + H_2O$$

C_2H_5OH CH_3CO_2H $CH_3CO_2C_2H_5$
(Ethanol)   (Ethanoic acid) (Ethyl ethanoate)

This compound formed as a result of the other parts of the two molecules combining is called an ester (ethyl ethanoate).

Many esters are pleasant smelling liquids used for flavouring essences; but esters having high molecular masses have a distinctly unpleasant odour.

Ethyl ethanoate is used as a solvent for glues and varnishes. Adhesives have the smell of ethyl ethanoate.

Ethyl ethanoate can be prepared in the laboratory as follows:

1. Mix together in a test tube $2cm^3$ ethanol and $1cm^3$ glacial ethanoic acid.

2. Add three drops of concentrated sulphuric acid to the mixture.

3. Heat the mixture by standing the test tube in a beaker of hot water for a few minutes.

4. Pour the warm mixture onto an equal volume of cold water in another beaker. An insoluble layer floats on the surface of the water and a sweet 'gluey' smell is obtained.

(b) Fats and oils are naturally occurring esters used as energy-storing compounds by plants and animals. Fats are esters of long chain alkanoic acids. The hydrolysis of an ester by an alkali is sometimes called saponification (soap-making).

Soap is manufactured by boiling and stirring (or heating by steam) a fat with sodium hydroxide solution for a long time.

Common salt is stirred into the mixture, before cooling, to separate the soap as an upper layer:

Fat	+	Alkali	→	Soap	+	Glycerine
Glyceryl stearate		Sodium hydroxide		Sodium stearate (sodium octadecanoate)		(Propanetriol)

The soap is scraped off and washed in running water to remove excess alkali. The propanetriol (glycerine or glycerol) is obtained by distillation. Because fats contain a mixture of fatty acids, soaps are, in practice, a mixture of the salts of fatty acids.

(c) Modern detergents have the following advantages over soap:

(i) They form no scum with hard water. If water is hard soap first reacts with dissolved calcium and magnesium compounds and forms a precipitate which forms a scum on the water:

Writing $NaOCT^-$ for sodium octadecanoate

then $Ca^{2+}(aq) + 2\ OCT^-(aq) \rightarrow CaOCT_2(s)$

or $\quad Mg^{2+}(aq) + 2\ OCT^-(aq) \rightarrow MgOCT_2(s)$

The scum itself is undesirable and its formation leads to the use of excessive quantities of soap. Detergents are more soluble than soap in water, form stable emulsions with grease and do not form a scum with hard water because their calcium and magnesium salts are soluble.

(ii) They are made from by-products of oil refining - unlike soap. Detergents are similar to soaps, both having molecules with polar and non-polar ends. The polar part of the detertent molecule is however different from the soap molecule in that it contains a sulphate or sulphonate group.

The long tailed hydrocarbons produced from the oil refining process are treated with sulphuric acid to form synthetic detergents (syndets).

Soaps are made from vegetable or animal fats. These are expensive and could be used for human consumption.

Question 23

(a) Sodium ions are detected by a flame test. An intense golden yellow flame indicates a sodium compound.

When sodium sulphite Na_2SO_3 is heated with dilute hydrochloric acid sulphur dioxide is evolved:

$$Na_2SO_3(s) + 2HCl(aq) \rightarrow 2NaCl(aq) + H_2O(l) + SO_2(g)$$

| White solid | Colourless | Sulphur |
| (H) | solution | dioxide |

When NaCl(aq) is evaporated to dryness a white solid NaCl(s) remains.
(I)

Test for sulphur dioxide: Turns filter paper which has been treated with acidified potassium dichromate (VI), from orange to green.

Substance H is sodium sulphite (Na_2SO_3).

Substance I is sodium chloride (NaCl).

(b) When copper oxide is reacted with nitric acid a blue solution of copper nitrate is formed:

$$2\,CuO(s) + 4\,HNO_3(aq) \rightarrow 2\,Cu(NO_3)_2(aq) + 2\,H_2O(l)$$

Black	Blue solution
powder	(K)
(J)	

On heating a blue solid remains: $2\,Cu(NO_3)_2(s)$
(Copper (II) nitrate)

On further heating:

$$2\,Cu(NO_3)_2(s) \rightarrow 2\,CuO(s) + 4\,NO_2(g) + O_2(g)$$

| Copper (II) | Black | Nitrogen | Oxygen |
| nitrate | powder | dioxide | |

Test for nitrogen dioxide: It is a reddish-brown gas which turns litmus red.

Substance J is copper (II) oxide (CuO).

Substance K is copper (II) nitrate ($Cu(NO_3)_2$).

(c) When iron is heated in dry hydrogen chloride, iron (II) chloride is formed and hydrogen gas is evolved:

$$Fe \ (s) + 2HCl \ (g) \rightarrow FeCl_2(s) + H_2 \ (g)$$

Metal   White
(L)   deliquescent
                 solid
                 (M)

When iron is heated in dry chlorine, iron (III) chloride is formed:

$$2 \ Fe \ (s) + 3Cl_2 \ (g) \rightarrow 2 \ FeCl_3 \ (s)$$

Metal   Deep red-black
(L)   solid
                 (N)

$FeCl_2$ dissolved in water with sodium hydroxide solution added forms iron (II) hydroxide:

$$Fe^{2+}(aq) + 2OH^-(aq) \rightarrow Fe(OH)_2 \ (s)$$
$$\text{Green}$$

$FeCl_3$ dissolved in water with sodium hydroxide solution added forms iron (III) hydroxide:

$$Fe^{3+}(aq) + 3OH^-(aq) \rightarrow Fe(OH)_3 \ (s)$$
$$\text{Reddish brown}$$

Test for hydrogen: A mixture of hydrogen and air explodes with a shrill 'pop' when lighted.

Substance L is the metal iron (Fe).

Substance M is iron (II) chloride ($FeCl_2$).

Substance N is iron (III) chloride ($FeCl_3$).

Question 24

(a) **Ammonia production** - Haber process. This is outlined in Question 18 (b)(ii). This process uses the reversible reaction between nitrogen and hydrogen gases (using a catalyst) to convert nitrogen of the air into ammonia: $N_2(g) + 3H_2(g) \rightleftharpoons 2NH_3(g)$.

The yield of ammonia is very low since the ammonia formed readily reverts into nitrogen and hydrogen once more by the reverse reaction. The optimum temperature and pressure to give an improved yield was determined (application of Le Chatelier's principle: 'When the conditions of a system at equilibrium are changed the system reacts in such a way as to oppose the effects of the change.') This led to the choice of a moderate temperature (500°C) and a high pressure (250 atmospheres) to give a good yield of ammonia.

Nitric acid is manufactured by the catalytic oxidation of ammonia (Ostwald process). Ammonia is mixed with about ten times its volume of air. It is then slightly compressed and passed over a platinum-rhodium catalyst at about 750°C.

$$4NH_3(g) + 5O_2(g) \rightarrow 4NO(g) + 6H_2O(l)$$

This is an exothermic reaction and maintains the catalyst temperature at about 750°C without additional heating. The ammonia is oxidised to nitrogen oxide. The gases are cooled and the nitrogen oxide reacts with the oxygen of the air to give nitrogen dioxide:

$$2NO(g) + O_2(g) \rightarrow 2NO_2(g)$$

The nitrogen dioxide combines with water and oxygen to yield aqueous nitric acid:

$$4NO_2(g) + O_2(g) + 2H_2O(l) \rightarrow 4HNO_3(aq)$$

(b) One of the more important chemical industries is fertiliser production. The main routes to compounds produced in the nitrogen industry are summarised in the diagram:

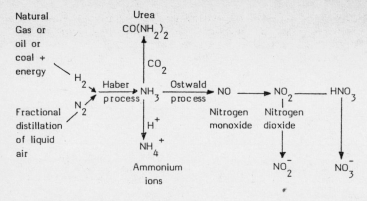

The two main steps are the fixation of atmospheric nitrogen to give ammonia and its oxidation to nitric oxide leading to nitric acid. The achievement of these reactions lead to the production of nitrogenous fertilizers (eg. ammonium nitrate)* , explosives, plastics and synthetic fibres. Urea $(CO(NH_2)_2)$ is of considerable industrial importance. It is sometimes directly used as a fertiliser since it is gradually hydrolysed in the soil with the production of CO_2 and NH_3. Urea is being increasingly used as a nitrogen fertiliser due to its high nitrogen content (46%) and slow release of useful nitrogen. In soil urea hydrolyses to ammonium carbonate

$$CO(NH_2)_2 + 2H_2O \rightarrow (NH_4)_2 CO_3$$

which undergoes rapid nitrification.

Nitrogen salts being more soluble than phosphates readily leach from soils into waterways (see Question 15(c)).

Nitrogen is a vital element for life as it is a constituent of amino acids from which proteins are formed.

*3/4 of the nitrogen produced is used to make ammonium nitrate (NH_4NO_3).

Before the advent of synthetic fertilizers the natural situation was as shown below (full line diagram).

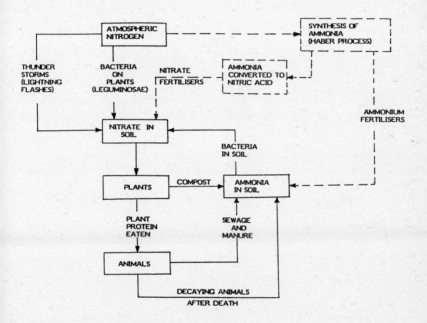

The natural fertilisers were animal manure and rotten plant compost and also the bacteria on leguminous plants which fix atmospheric nitrogen and convert it to ammonia and nitrates.

This situation no longer holds because the bulk of the population lives in towns and cities far from the areas of food production. The sewage which is dumped in rivers could be used as fertiliser locally but not on a global scale (cost of transportation etc.).

Synthetic fertilisers restore the natural balance. Without them the world could not sustain the population it has. The modified nitrogen cycle is shown in dotted lines on the diagram.

Crop yields can be greatly increased by the use of chemical fertilisers. The primary nutrients, nitrogen, phosphorous, potassium (NPK) along with secondary nutrients, calcium, magnesium and sulphur plus trace elements are usually included in compound fertilisers. Care is needed to ensure that these compound fertilisers are not wasted by excessive use with the resultant risk of pollution.

(c) Sodium nitrate $NaNO_3$

Formula weight $= 23 + 14 + (3 \times 16)$

$$= 85$$

$\therefore$ % nitrogen $= \dfrac{14}{85} \times 100 =$ **16.47%**

Ammonium sulphate $(NH_4)_2 SO_4$

Formula weight $= (14 + 4 \times 1) \times 2 + 32 + (4 \times 16)$

$$= 28 + 8 + 32 + 64$$

$$= 132$$

$\therefore$ % nitrogen $= \dfrac{23}{132} \times 100 =$ **21.21%**

In terms of the nitrogen content the better fertiliser is ammonium sulphate.

Question 25

(a) Metals/metallic oxides eg. copper oxide dissolve in dilute acid. Non-metals eg. carbon will not dissolve in dilute acid.

(i) Add the copper oxide/carbon mixture to an excess of 2M dilute sulphuric acid in a beaker. Gently heat for a few minutes and then boil for approximately ten minutes [great care must be exercised throughout]. The carbon does not react with the acid but the copper oxide does:

$$CuO \text{ (s)} + H_2SO_4 \text{(aq)} \rightarrow CuSO_4 \text{(aq)} + H_2O \text{(l)}$$

The carbon can then be filtered off, washed and dried.

(ii) Add 2M NaOH solution to the filtrate:

$$CuSO_4 \text{(aq)} + 2NaOH \text{(aq)} \rightarrow Na_2SO_4 \text{(aq)} + Cu(OH)_2 \text{(s)}$$

Copper hydroxide is precipitated.

Boil the mixture for some minutes; the precipitate changes to black copper (II) oxide:

$$Cu(OH)_2 \text{(s)} \rightarrow CuO \text{ (s)} + H_2O \text{(l)}$$

Allow the precipitate to settle. The copper (II) oxide can then be filtered off, washed and dried.

(b) Solids, like liquids, will vaporise at all temperatures. The passage of a substance from the solid state directly into the vapour state and its recondensation into a solid, is termed sublimation. Ammonium chloride dissociates on heating into ammonia and hydrogen chloride which recombine on cooling

$$NH_4Cl \text{ (s)} \rightleftharpoons NH_3 \text{(g)} + HCl \text{ (g)} \qquad \text{Endothermic}$$

Place the mixture of ammonium and sodium chlorides in an evaporating basin and cover the basin with a filter paper in which holes have been pierced.

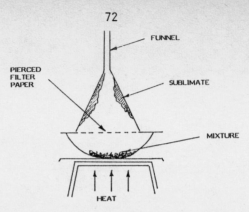

Place an inverted funnel on the filter paper. Initially heat the mixture slowly and then strongly to drive off the last traces of ammonium chloride. The ammonium chloride sublimes, passes through the holes in the filter paper and condenses on the cool parts of the funnel. The residue is sodium chloride.

(c) Chromatography (colour writing) is a process for the separation of a mixture of solutes by their different rates of movement over a porous medium, caused by a moving solvent. To separate the dyes ascending strip or partition chromatography can be used.

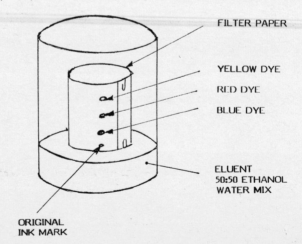

A small drop of the black ink is placed at the bottom of the filter paper and is allowed to dry. The paper is then folded into the shape of a cylinder, secured

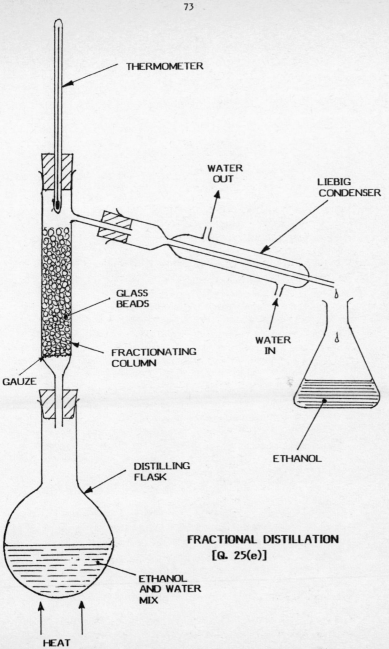

THERMOMETER

WATER OUT

LIEBIG CONDENSER

GLASS BEADS

FRACTIONATING COLUMN

GAUZE

WATER IN

ETHANOL

DISTILLING FLASK

FRACTIONAL DISTILLATION
[Q. 25(e)]

ETHANOL AND WATER MIX

HEAT

with paperclips and placed into a beaker containing a solvent:water mixture (eluent).

The eluent must be below the original ink mark. The beaker is covered up and left undisturbed. The eluent steadily soaks into the paper travelling up to the top by capillary action. Some of the coloured dyes in the ink drop dissolve better than others as the eluent passes and these get carried further up the paper. The more soluble dyes move the shortest distance up the paper.

(d) Pass the mixture of gases through concentrated potassium hydroxide. The carbon dioxide gas is dissolved leaving carbon monoxide gas. The carbon monoxide gas is insoluble in the alkali.

$$2\ KOH(aq) + CO_2(g) \rightarrow K_2CO_3(aq) + H_2O(l)$$

Potassium hydroxide is used in preference to sodium hydroxide for absorbing carbon dioxide because potassium carbonate is more soluble than sodium carbonate and so there is less chance of it being deposited.

(e) Fractional distillation is used to separate a mixture of miscible liquids - in this case ethanol and water.

The fractionating column, shown in diagram, has a large cooling surface and in it the vapour passing up from the boiling liquid meets the colder condensed liquid dropping down. The glass beads ensure that the vapour and liquid mix well. The less volatile part (water) of the vapour condenses and the more volatile part (ethanol) of the liquid evaporates.

This process takes place everywhere inside the column; in effect continuous evaporation and condensation is taking place in it.

The vapour at the top is almost pure ethanol (96% ethanol, 4% water). The liquid in the distilling flask becomes richer in water and finally is almost pure water.

Question 26

(a) (i) Electrolysis is the decomposition of an electrolyte by the passage of an electric current through it.

(ii) Electrolyte. An electrolyte is a compound which when molten and/or in solution, conducts an electric current and is decomposed by it.

(iii) Non-electrolyte. A non-electrolyte is a compound which does not conduct an electric current, either when molten or in solution, since no ions are present, eg sugar, methylbenzene (toluene), ethanol.

(iv) Strong electrolyte. A strong electrolyte is one in which ionisation is complete or almost complete in solution, eg:

(1) Salts - completely ionised, even in the solid state.

(2) Potassium and sodium hydroxides - completely ionised even in the solid state.

(3) Sulphuric acid, nitric acid and hydrochloric acid - covalent in the absence of water.

(v) Weak electrolyte. A weak electrolyte is one in which ionisation in solution is slight, the solution containing mainly un-ionised molecules eg

(1) Organic acids such as ethanoic acid

$$CH_3COOH(aq) \rightleftharpoons CH_3COO^-(aq) + H^+(aq)$$

(2) Ammonia solution

$$NH_3(g) + H_2O(l) \rightleftharpoons NH_4^+(aq) + OH^-(aq)$$

(3) Water is a very weak electrolyte. One molecule in about 550 million ionises as shown:

$$H_2O(l) \rightleftharpoons H^+(aq) + OH^-(aq)$$

$$2H_2O(l) \rightleftharpoons H_3O^+(aq) + OH^-(aq)$$

    (vi) **Anion.**   Negatively charged ions are attracted to the anode (positive electrode) and are called anions.

    (vii) **Cation.**   Positively charged ions are attracted to the cathode (negative electrode) and are called cations.

Since **electrons** are **removed** at the **anode** the process taking place is **oxidation.**   At the **cathode electrons** are **added** and so **reduction** is occurring.

(b)

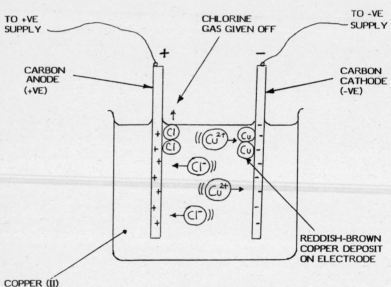

ELECTROLYSIS OF COPPER (II) CHLORIDE SOLUTION

Ions attracted to anode from copper (II) chloride = Cl^-(aq)

Ions attracted to anode from water = OH^- (aq)

Ions attracted to cathode from copper (II) chloride = Cu^{2+}(aq)

Ions attracted to cathode from water = H^+(aq)

At the anode: For every electron taken from the cathode, electrons are given to the anode by chloride ions. The result is the formation of chlorine atoms. These form into molecules and become bubbles of chlorine gas.

At the cathode: The positive copper ions travel to the cathode, collect electrons and become ordinary copper atoms. These collect together to form a deposit of copper.

$$2Cl^-(aq) \rightarrow 2Cl(g) + 2e^- \quad | \quad \rightarrow 2e^- + Cu^{2+}(aq) \rightarrow Cu(s)$$
$$\downarrow$$
$$Cl_2(g)$$

At anode	At cathode
Loss of electrons	Gain of electrons
(oxidation)	(reduction)

Chlorine is formed at the anode which must be of carbon as chlorine reacts with most other elements.

Copper is deposited at the cathode. The copper chloride solution gradually becomes more dilute.

Question 27

(a) Hydrogen and oxygen react together to form water. For every mole of hydrogen molecules burnt 286 kJ of energy is released ie. the system loses energy to the surroundings and the energy change ΔH is **negative (exothermic).**

(A) ...... $H_2(g) + 1/2\ O_2(g) \rightarrow H_2O(l)$; $\Delta H = -286\ kJ$

(B) ...... $2H_2(g) + O_2(g) \rightarrow 2H_2O(l)$; $\Delta H = -572\ kJ$

[Note the different number of moles and the different values of energy for equations (A) and (B)]

In energy level diagram (1) the amount of energy change is the heat of combustion ΔHc of hydrogen. The heat of combustion value is given for the mole of H_2 burnt in oxygen. **Reaction mixtures in combustion always lose energy to the surroundings.**

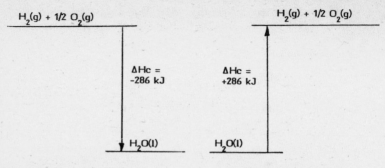

(1) ENERGY LEVEL DIAGRAM FOR EQUATION A (COMBUSTION)

(2) ENERGY LEVEL DIAGRAM FOR EQUATION A (DECOMPOSITION)

In energy level diagram (2) the amount of energy change is for decomposition of H_2O and shows that 286 kJ of energy must be supplied to change one mole of H_2O back to hydrogen and oxygen.

The principle of conservation of energy states that energy can neither be created nor destroyed but can only be changed into different forms of energy ie. energy is conserved.

Therefore the amount of energy released on the formation of one mole of H_2O is exactly the same as the amount of energy required to decompose one mole of H_2O.

This is indicated in the energy diagrams, the sign of ΔH being reversed.

(b)   Let 100 cm^3 of water = 100g (density of water is taken as 1g cm^{-3})

Also as 1K ≒ 1°C then 10K ≒ 10°C

Energy change in water = specific heat capacity x mass x change in temperature

Energy change in water = 4.2 J g^{-1}°C^{-1} x 100g x 10°C

Energy change in water = 4200 J

One mole of NaOH = (23 + 16 + 1) = 40g

$\therefore$ 4g of NaOH $= \dfrac{4}{40} = 0.1$ mole

$\therefore$ 0.1 mole of NaOH took 4200 J of energy to dissolve.

$\therefore$ One mole of NaOH takes $\dfrac{4200}{0.1} = 42000$ J of energy

Since energy is given to the water the reaction is exothermic and ΔH will be negative.

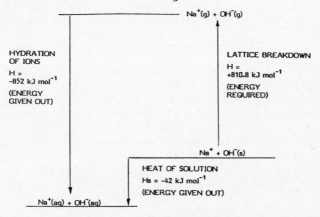

HYDRATION OF IONS
H = -852 kJ mol^{-1}
(ENERGY GIVEN OUT)

Na$^+$(g) + OH$^-$(g)

LATTICE BREAKDOWN
H = +810.8 kJ mol^{-1}
(ENERGY REQUIRED)

Na$^+$ + OH$^-$(s)

HEAT OF SOLUTION
Hs = -42 kJ mol^{-1}
(ENERGY GIVEN OUT)

Na$^+$(aq) + OH$^-$(aq)

ENERGY LEVEL DIAGRAM (SODIUM HYDROXIDE)

On dissolving an ionic substance in water energy is required to break down the crystal lattice and separate the ions. On separation the ions become **hydrated*** and energy is given out (exothermic).

In this case, as shown in the energy level diagram, the energy required to break down the crystal lattice is less than that required for hydration of the ions. Therefore the overall reaction is exothermic.

*As the crystal breaks down the ions go into solution and are surrounded by water molecules, ie the ions are said to be hydrated. Also if the force of attraction between the water molecules and the ions is greater than the forces holding the ions together in the crystal then the ionic solid will be quite soluble in water.

Question 28

(a) When powdered sulphur is heated, the lemon-yellow solid melts at 113ºC giving a straw coloured liquid which flows easily like water. Solid and liquid sulphur possess a ring of eight atoms, S_8, in each molecule.

At about 160ºC the liquid becomes reddish-brown and viscous. It remains like syrup in the tube even when the tube is inverted. The changes are caused by the rings of 8 atoms opening and the ends joining to others to form long chains*, some with 10,000 atoms, which become entwined.

On warming further the colour lightens slightly and the liquid becomes less viscous. This is due to the long chains breaking down and becoming shorter.

The liquid boils at 444ºC (717K) and forms a brownish vapour. On cold surfaces the vapour condenses directly to a yellow sublimate known as 'flowers of sulphur' consisting of S_8 and chain molecules.

At 1000ºC the vapour is S_2 molecules and at higher temperatures the molecules are monatomic, S.

S, S_2 and S_8 are gaseous allotropes.

(b) Two facts prove that rhombic and monoclinic sulphur are allotropes:

1. One gram of either rhombic or monoclinic sulphur will burn in oxygen to yield the same mass (2g) of sulphur dioxide and nothing else.

2. One gram of monoclinic sulphur changes slowly at room temperature into one gram of rhombic sulphur.

Differences between allotropes

Monoclinic (prismatic) sulphur.	Rhombic (octahedral) sulphur.
Pale yellow. M.P. 120ºC Needle shaped crystals. Stable above 96ºC. Density 1.98g/cm^3.	Bright yellow. M.P. 113ºC. Diamond shaped crystals. Stable below 96ºC. Density 2.06g/cm^3.

(c) One mole of any gas occupies 22.4 dm^3 at standard temperature and pressure (0°C and one atmosphere (760 mm Hg)).

From $\dfrac{P_1V_1}{T_1} = \dfrac{P_2V_2}{T_2}$

P_1 = 760 mm Hg

V_1 = ?

T_1 = 0°C (273K)

P_2 = 722 mm Hg

V_2 = 7 dm^3

T_2 = 182°C (455K)

$\dfrac{760\text{mm Hg} \times V_1}{273K}$

$= \dfrac{722\text{mm Hg} \times 7\ dm^3}{455K}$

$722 \times 7 \times 273 = 760 \times 455 \times V_1$

$V_1 = \dfrac{722 \times 7 \times 273}{760 \times 455} = \dfrac{1379742}{345800} = 3.99\ dm^3$

Molar mass of SO_2 = 32 + (16x2) = 64

ie. 1 mole of SO_2 contains 32g of sulphur

ie. 1 mole of SO_2 (22.4 dm^3) contain 32g sulphur

$\therefore$ 3.99 dm^3 of SO_2 contains

$\dfrac{3.99}{22.4} \times 32g = 0.178 \times 32 = 5.7g$ of sulphur

*polymerization

Question 29

(a) (i)   A **saturated solution** is one which contains as much solute as can be dissolved at the temperature concerned in the presence of undissolved solute.

     (ii) A **supersaturated solution** is one which contains more solute than a saturated solution at the same temperature.

(iii) The **solubility of a solute** in a solvent at a particular temperature is the mass of solute required to saturate 100g of solvent at that temperature.

Solubility curves are useful for finding out how much solvent will dissolve in a known mass of solvent at a given temperature. They are also useful in predicting the mass of crystals which will be deposited on cooling a solution of known concentration over a particular temperature range.

(b) (i) The amount of potassium nitrate separating out on cooling to 20°C is (135 - 32) = 103g ie. 103g of crystals is obtained. Pure nitrate is therefore obtained from the mixture.

No sodium chloride separates because the solution is not saturated with it.

(ii) The amount of potassium nitrate separating out on cooling to 20°C is (95 - 32) = 63g ie. 63g of crystals is obtained.

As only 37g of the chloride dissolves then (95 - 37) = 58g can be separated. When cooled to 20°C (37 - 35) = 2g of the chloride separate out.

(iii) The amount of potassium chlorate separating out on cooling to 20°C is (32 - 8) = 24g ie. 24g of crystals is obtained.

No potassium chloride separates out because the solution is not saturated with it.

Question 30

(a) Rain dissolves some CO_2 as it falls through the air and may also collect more as it passes through soil which contains decaying vegetation. **Rainwater is therefore very dilute carbonic acid.**

$$H_2O \text{ (l)} + CO_2\text{(g)} \rightleftharpoons H_2CO_3 \text{ (aq)}$$

This water may pass through chalk or limestone and although calcium carbonate is not soluble it will react with water containing CO_2 to form soluble calcium hydrogen carbonate.

$$CaCO_3(s) + CO_2(g) + H_2O(l) \rightarrow Ca(HCO_3)_2(aq)$$

Calcium
carbonate
(insoluble)

Calcium
hydrogen carbonate
(soluble)

$$MgCO_3(s) + CO_2(g) + H_2O(l) \rightarrow Mg(HCO_3)_2(aq)$$

Magnesium
carbonate
(insoluble)

Magnesium
hydrogen carbonate
(soluble)

This water will be temporarily hard.

Water that passes through rocks containing calcium sulphate or magnesium sulphate will dissolve some of the salt. **Such water will be permanently hard.**

ie. **Temporary hardness is caused by** calcium hydrogen carbonate or magnesium hydrogen carbonate.

Permanent hardness is caused by any of the salts calcium or magnesium sulphate or calcium or magnesium chloride.

The difference between temporarily hard water and permanently hard water is that temporarily hard water can be made soft by boiling whilst permanently hard water cannot.

(b) As previously stated temporary hardness is removed by boiling the water. Boiling changes hydrogen carbonates to insoluble carbonates.

$$Ca(HCO_3)_2(aq) \rightarrow CaCO_3(s) + H_2O(l) + CO_2(g)$$

This reaction happens inside a kettle over and over again when temporarily hard water is boiled. The calcium carbonate deposited is called 'fur'. The boiling has made the water soft and a lather can now be formed with soap.

Other methods of softening water removes both kinds of hardness:

(i) **Addition of sodium carbonate (washing soda).** This changes the soluble calcium and magnesium salts to insoluble carbonates:

$$CaSO_4(aq) + Na_2CO_3(aq) \rightarrow CaCO_3(s) + Na_2SO_4(aq)$$

$$Ca(HCO_3)(aq) + Na_2CO_3(aq) \rightarrow CaCO_3(s) + 2NaHCO_3(aq)$$

This is why washing soda crystals ($Na_2CO_3 .10H_2O$) were used before detergents were manufactured.

(ii) **Base exchange.** Hard water can be made soft with a substance called a zeolite which is a naturally occurring form of sodium aluminium silicate. As water flows over it the zeolite removes the calcium from the water in exchange for sodium.

Letting X represent the aluminium silicate radical

$$Na_2X + CaSO_4 \rightarrow CaX + Na_2SO_4$$

(Zeolite) (Calcium (Calcium (Sodium
          Salt)   salt of   salt)
                  zeolite)

$$X^{2-}(aq) + Ca^{2+}(aq) \rightarrow CaX(s)$$

After a time the zeolite is all used up, ie. changed to calcium aluminium silicate. The zeolite can be recovered by running a solution of concentrated sodium chloride through it:

$$CaX + 2NaCl \rightarrow Na_2X + CaCl_2$$

(Spent   (Restored
 zeolite)   zeolite)

$$X_2^-(aq) + 2Na^+(aq) \rightarrow Na_2X(s)$$

The calcium chloride formed is washed away and therefore the zeolite can be used over and over again.

(iii) **Distillation.** This removes all hardness but is an expensive method.

(c) **Disadvantages**

(i) **Wastes soap.** Hard water needs a great deal of soap before it forms a lather. (See also

Question 22(c) (i) and (ii).)

(ii) **It forms a 'fur'** in pans and kettles (part (b) of this question) and deposits of scale in boilers.

Advantages

(i) The calcium compounds in hard water may help to form **healthy teeth and bones** as these contain calcium compounds, usually calcium phosphate.

(ii) **Shells of animals.** The shells and eggs of many animals contain calcium carbonate. Snails obtain calcium from hard water.

THE BASIC CONCEPTS SERIES

The Basic Concepts series attempts to explain in a clear and concise manner the main concepts involved in a subject. Paragraphs are numbered for ease of reference and key points are emboldened for clear identification, with self assessment questions at the end of each chapter. The texts should prove useful to students studying for A level, professional and first year degree courses. Other titles in the series include:—

Basic Concepts in Business by Tony Hines
Basic Concepts in Foundation Accounting by Tony Hines
Basic Concepts in Financial Mathematics and Statistics
    by T.M. Jackson
Basic Concepts in Business Taxation by K. Astbury

QUESTIONS AND ANSWERS SERIES

These highly successful revision aids contain questions and answers based on actual examination questions and provide fully worked answers for each question. The books are written by experienced lecturers and examiners and will be useful for students preparing for O and A level, foundation and BTEC examinations. Subjects include:—

Economics by G. Walker
Accounting by T. Hines
Multiple Choice Economics by Dr. S. Kermally
O level Mathematics by R.H. Evans
A level Pure Mathematics and Statistics by R.H. Evans
A level Pure and Applied Mathematics by R.H. Evans
O level Physics by R.H. Evans
O level Chemistry by J. Sheen
O level Human Biology by D. Reese